THE STEROID
BIBLE
THIRD EDITION

Belle International
P.O. Box 160233
Sacramento, CA 95816
Copyright ® 1997
ISBN 1-890342-00-9: $24.95

TABLE OF CONTENTS

INTRODUCTION

Anabolic steroid use is widespread. A drug once limited to an elite group of highly competitive athletes has infiltrated our society to the point where teenagers have started experimenting with it. Today, motivations ranging from being the worlds' best athlete in a certain event to developing big muscles in order to impress girls at school are driving people to use anabolic steroids. Anabolic steroids now appeal to a wider group of people than ever before. Under such circumstances, education is essential.

The medical community did athletes a great disservice for many years by failing to recognize that anabolic steroids, coupled with intense physical exercise, can increase muscle size and strength. Today, the majority of the medical community acknowledges that anabolic steroids can increase muscle size and strength. However, the medical communities' delay in recognizing these facts created a legacy of distrust between athletes and doctors that exists to this day.

While the medical community proved its ignorance by failing to recognize the positive effects of anabolic steroids many athletes refused to believe that anabolic steroids could cause serious negative side effects. At present, the consensus is that anabolic steroid use can cause serious psychological and physical problems. As a result, anabolic steroids were recently reclassified as schedule III controlled substances. Unfortunately, it is hard, if not impossible, to say that if one takes X milligrams of a certain anabolic steroid one will have an X% chance of suffering from certain side effects. Disagreement on the likelihood of suffering from serious side effects of anabolic steroid use is a force that continues to promote distrust between doctors and athletes. Many athletes now recognize that anabolic steroids can lead to serious side effects. However, athletes tend to believe that doctors over estimate the likelihood that one will experience these serious negative side effects.

The problem is further complicated by the legal ramifications of conducting carefully monitored studies on athletes that are taking high doses of anabolic steroids. Such studies would offer accurate statistics on the dangers and benefits of steroid use. However, it is illegal for doctors to conduct such studies because anabolic steroids can only be used, legally, to treat specific health problems. In addition, many of the side effects of anabolic steroid use could take decades to show up. Even if doctors were allowed to start studies today, which is highly unlikely, it could take decades to complete the studies.

Under these circumstances it is easy to understand how widely differing opinions about anabolic steroid use can exist. This book attempts to cut through the confusion by telling the truth about anabolic steroids. If you are thinking about using anabolic steroids, this book will present you with facts that will allow you to make an educated decision. If you use anabolic steroids, this book will give you advice that will make your life much safer. If you are trying to get off of anabolic steroids, this book can help you. This book is not meant to shove an opinion about anabolic steroid use down your throat. Rather, you will be presented with facts and allowed to make your own decision.

The decision you make will require you to weigh the benefits and drawbacks of anabolic steroid use. The primary benefits, increases in muscle size and strength, must be compared with the possibility of suffering from some of the negative side effects of anabolic steroid use such as roid rage gynecomastia, and liver tumors. In addition, it should be noted that gains made while using anabolic steroids are usually lost once anabolic steroid use is discontinued. This book will allow you to draw an accurate picture of the risk/benefit ratio of anabolic steroid use. When you have finished reading this book you will be able to make an educated decision about anabolic steroid use, a decision that will be right for you.

1

HOW ANABOLIC STEROIDS WORK

Scientists have known for many years that the testes play a major role in the development of masculine features. In the 1800's scientists proved this fact by transplanting testes from a cock to a hen and observing the results. As suspected, the hen developed masculine characteristics. Testosterone, the specific hormone responsible for this masculinization, was not isolated until 1935.[1]

German scientists, working during World War II, were the first to synthesize anabolic steroids.[2] The Germans are believed to have carried out massive experiments on human prisoners involving anabolic steroids. The results of these experiments have been lost as they were never published. Some personal accounts from the war suggest that the Germans gave anabolic steroids to their troops in order to increase their aggressiveness. It is known for a fact, from the records of Adolf Hitler's personal physician, that Hitler took anabolic steroids. There is speculation that Hitler's anabolic steroid use may have amplified his aggressive personality.[3]

Testosterone, like all anabolic steroids, has both anabolic, tissue building, and androgenic, masculinizing, effects. This means that all anabolic steroids, in addition to promoting tissue building, promote masculinization. The masculinizing effects of anabolic steroids are powerful deterrents to steroid use among women. However, a significant number of women, primarily due to the fact that female sports have become extremely competitive, take anabolic steroids. Serious problems that can arise from anabolic steroid use by women are discussed in later portions of this book.

Scientists have tried to isolate testosterone's anabolic properties in order to develop a drug that promotes tissue building without causing masculinizing effects. This has turned out to be a difficult task because it is likely that these effects result from the same action in different tissue.[4] This task has not yet been, and probably never will be, successfully completed. As a result, anabolic androgenic steroids is a better name for anabolic steroids as all anabolic steroids have inseparable tissue building and masculinizing effects.

Synthetic anabolic steroids were created by making small modifications to the testosterone molecule. The slight differences that these modifications create gives different types of anabolic steroids slightly different properties. For example, some anabolic steroids are less masuculinizing than others. Anavar is an anabolic steroid that has weak masculinizing effects. As a result, Anavar is popular among female anabolic steroid users. However, if a steroid has weak masculinizing effects it is likely that the steroid has weak tissue building effects. This supports the idea that the tissue building and masculinizing effects of anabolic steroids are probably inseparable because they stem from the same action in different tissue.

Modifications to the testosterone molecule have also served to create anabolic steroids that are processed at slower rates. When free testosterone (testosterone that has not been chemically modified) is given orally it is immediately degraded by the liver. When taken orally, free testosterone reaches the liver before it reaches skeletal muscle. 98% of orally administered free testosterone is degraded and inactivated during its first passage through the liver. Injected(parenteral) free testosterone reaches skeletal muscle before reaching the liver. However, injected free testosterone is also 98% degraded and inactivated during its first passage through the liver.

In order for an anabolic steroid to be effective it must be able to travel through the blood stream many times before being inactivated. Modifying the testosterone molecule by adding a group of elements, an alkyl group, at a specific location, known as the 17 α-position, has resulted in anabolic steroids that are harder for the liver to process. Steroids that have been modified in this manner have to pass through the liver many times before they are inactivated. This allows a much larger amount of these steroids to reach skeletal muscle and produce the desired effects. However, it also forces the liver to work harder. Most oral anabolic steroids have been modified in this manner. These oral anabolic steroids can cause liver damage. Most injectable anabolic steroids are not modified in this manner. Injectable anabolic steroids, in general, are safer because they are less harsh on the liver. However, some injectable anabolic steroids like Winstrol, stanozolol, (also produced in an orally effective form) are chemically comparable to oral anabolic steroids and have the same effects as oral anabolic steroids.

The majority of injectable anabolic steroids are testosterone esters. An ester is a compound produced by the reaction between an acid and an alcohol. Esterification of testosterone makes testosterone effective even if it only makes one passage through the blood stream before being inactivated by the liver. Most testosterone esters are injected intramuscularly so that they reach skeletal muscle before reaching the liver. Testosterone esters are longer acting and safer than other usually orally administered anabolic steroids that have an alkyl group at the 17 α position. There are a few testosterone esters, methenolone acetate and testosterone undecanoate, that can be taken orally.[5] It is not clear why methenolone acetate is orally effective. Testosterone undecanoate enters the blood stream through the lymphatic system, so that it largely bypasses the liver.[6] Methenolone acetate and testosterone undecanoate are less harsh on the liver than other oral anabolic steroids.

Scientists have created many different synthetic anabolic steroids by modifying the testosterone molecule. Specific properties of some of these steroids are listed below.

Dihydrotestosterone
Dihydrotestosterone is not toxic to the liver(hepatotoxic), and is

given by injection or transdermally. It has been used to treat gynecomastia, female breast development, because it can not be converted to estrogen, a female hormone. Gynecomastia occurs when naturally occurring testosterone production and synthetic anabolic steroid levels reach such a low level that female hormones start to dominate. Female hormones exist naturally in men and a small amount of most synthetic anabolic steroids are converted to female hormones when used. Dihydrotestosterone restores the proper dominance of male hormones while causing no increases in the level of female hormones. Gynecomastia is discussed in greater detail in the next chapter

Fluoxymesterone

Fluoxymesterone, brand name Halotestin, is an oral anabolic steroid. Its masculinizing effect has been enhanced by the introduction of fluorine and the addition of a hydroxy group into the steroid skeleton of testosterone. It is toxic to the liver because it contains a 17 α methyl group.

Mesterolone

Mesterolone, brand name Androviron, is an orally effective anabolic steroid derived from androstenedione. It can not be converted to estrogen in peripheral tissue, dose not appear to cause liver damage when given in normal doses, and does not completely shut down the body's natural production of gonadotropin.[7] Gonadotropin is a hormone produced by the testes that stimulates testosterone production.

Methandrostenolone

Methandrostenolone, brand name Dianabol, is an orally effective, anabolic steroid that is toxic to the liver. It has also been produced in an injectable form. Dianabol was once one of the most widely produced anabolic steroids. The Ciba Pharmaceutical Company released Dianabol in 1958 making it the first anabolic steroid that was widely available in the Untied States. A catchy slogan, "Dianabol, the breakfast of champions", gained popularity among athletes and helped to fuel demand for the drug. Production has decreased sharply in recent years due to

Dianabol's strong liver damaging effects and the discovery of safer, more effective testosterone esters. As a result, it is likely that most of the Dianabol on the black-market is fake.

Methenolone acetate

Methenolone acetate, brand name Primobolan, is one of the few orally effective testosterone esters. It is not toxic to the liver.

Methyltestosterone

Methyltestosterone, brand name Metandren, is an oral anabolic steroid. It was modified at the 17 α position in order to make it orally effective. Methyltestosterone is absorbed quickly and maximal blood levels are observed 90 to 120 minutes after ingestion. Methyltestosterone has a 150 minute half life in blood.[8] The alkyl group at the 17 α position of methyltestosterone gives it toxic properties that primarily effect the liver. Many doctors have recommended that methyltestosterone no longer be use therapeutically due to its toxic effects.[9] These doctors argue that other, safer steroids can be used instead of methyltestosterone.

Nandrolone decanoate

Nandrolone decanoate, brand name Deca-Durabolin, is an injectable testosterone ester that is not toxic to the liver. It is popular among athletes because it has decreased androgenic effects, increased anabolic effects, and remains active for a long time. However, it is also responsible for a large number of positive drug tests. Its metabolites remain detectable in the urine for up to 12 weeks in some individuals.

Oxandrolone

Oxandrolone, brand name Anavar, is an orally effective anabolic steroid. It is toxic to the liver. Its weak masculinizing effects when used at low dosages and relatively fast clearing time make it popular among male and female athletes. Anavar has significant masculinizing effects when used at high dosages.

Oxymethelone

Oxymethelone, brand name Anadrol-50, is an oral anabolic steroid that is toxic to the liver.

Stanozolol

Stanozolol, brand name Winstrol, is an anabolic steroid that is available in oral and injectable forms. It is toxic to the liver in both forms due to the addition of an alkyl group at the 17 α position. Its moderate masculinizing effects make it more popular among women than other, more androgenic anabolic steroids. Stanozolol is the steroid that Ben Johnson tested positive for at the 1988 Olympics in Seoul Korea. Charlie Francis, Ben Johnson's coach, stated that he knew the proper clearance time for Stanozolol. Francis offered a number of theories for Johnson's positive ranging from sabotage to Johnson taking stanozolol from his own private stash.[10]

Testosterone cyclohexanecarboxylate

Testosterone cyclohexanecarboxylate, is an intramuscularly injectable testosterone ester. It is one of the longest lasting testosterone esters. It is usually administered in 2 week intervals for testosterone replacement therapy.

Testosterone cypionate

Testosterone cypionate, brand name Depo-testosterone, is an intramuscularly injectable testosterone ester. It is one of the longest lasting testosterone esters. It is usually administered in 2 week intervals for testosterone replacement therapy.

Testosterone enanthate

Testosterone enanthate, brand name Delatestryl, is an intramuscularly injectable testosterone ester. It is one of the longest lasting testosterone esters. It is usually administered in 2 week intervals for testosterone replacement therapy.

Testosterone propionate

Testosterone propionate, brand name Testex, is an intramuscularly injectable testosterone ester. It is not toxic to the liver and it is frequently used for therapeutic treatments. Its main draw back is that it gets inactivated quickly and therefore needs to be administered frequently. When used for testosterone replacement therapy testosterone propionate injections are administered at two to three day intervals.

Testosterone-trans-4-n-butylcyclohexyl-carboxylate

Testosterone-trans-4-n-butylcyclohexyl-carboxylate, code name 20Aet-1, is a testosterone ester that was developed by the World Health Organization for possible use as a male contraceptive. In clinical trials a single 40 mg injection raised a castrated monkey's testosterone level into the normal range for about 4 months.[11]

Testosterone undecanoate

Testosterone undecanoate is one of the few orally effective testosterone esters. Absorption is improved if it is taken in arachis oil and with a meal.[12] It is not toxic to the liver because it dose not have a 17α methyl group. It is one of the preferred drugs for hormone replacement therapy because it is relatively safe. The only major draw back to testosterone undecanoate is that it must be taken in high doses to be effective. 40 mg of testosterone undecanoate given 2 to 4 times daily are required as treatment for men that need testosterone replacement therapy.[13]

Anabolic steroids are used to treat hypogonadal men. Hypogonadal men are men that have damaged testes, undescended testes, or no testes at all. Hypogaonadal men have extremely low testosterone levels because their damaged or non existent testes are unable to produce proper testosterone levels. Normal men produce about 7 mg of testosterone per day. "For testosterone substitution purposes in hypogonadal men testosterone propionate must be injected every 2 to 3 days while testosterone enanthate, when given in doses of 200 to 250 mg, allows spacing of the injection at about 2 week intervals. Two other clinically available testosterone esters, testosterone cypionate and testosterone cyclohexanecarboxylate have very similar kinetic properties so that they can be used in the same doses and intervals."[14] This is currently the most common form of treatment for hypogonadal men. It does not produce testosterone serum levels that are as steady as those that occur in healthy men. Patients are aware of these fluctuations in testosterone levels because such fluctuations effect their sexual activity and emotional state. New testosterone preparations have been developed in an attempt to avoid these shortcomings. A new testosterone ester, testosterone-trans-4-n-butylcyclohexly-carboxylate, code name 20Aet-1, was tested in laboratory rodents and then castrated monkeys. When a single 40 mg dose of this ester was injected into castrated monkeys it raised the testosterone serum levels of the animals into the normal range for about 4 months.[15]

Testosterone levels decrease as men age. The practice of using testosterone replacement therapy to boost a normal male's decreasing testosterone levels is a recently accepted medicinal use for steroids that makes steroids readily available to a large portion of the population. It is not uncommon for men in their 40s, 50s, and 60s to experience decreased sexual desire, depression, mood swings, and a gradual decrease in muscle mass and strength. These changes are now recognized as symptoms of a condition that has only recently been documented, male menopause.

The word menopause is derived from two Greek words, men, month, and pausis, cessation. This makes sense as menopause is marked by the cessation of the monthly cycle in women. In other words, women no longer have periods when they enter menopause. In men the situation is some what different. Male reproductive glands do not shut down the way a women's ovaries do. The process is much more gradual and it does not occur in all men. As a result, the medical community has only recently recognized the phenomenon of male menopause. On the other hand, female menopause has been recognized and treated for several decades.

A large portion of men can father children well into their latter years. However, male sexual changes in middle age often produce a virility crisis. In addition to male menopause, the terms viropause and andropause are used to describe this phenomenon.

The *Massachusetts Male Aging Study* conducted from 1984-1989 looked at a cross-sectional, random sample of 1709 men between the ages of 40 and 70. Subjects were interviewed about demographics and life-style, were surveyed regarding a variety of physical factors, and were asked to complete a questionnaire about sexual activity.

According to their self-reports, 51 percent of normal, healthy males in this age group experience some degree of impotence. The steepest change over the 30 year age span was in the onset of moderate impotence. Moderate impotence is defined as having problems with erections half of the time. The prevalence of total impotence tripled from five percent at age 40 to 15 percent at age 70.

Extrapolating those numbers to the general U.S. population of the same age group (39 million men in 1993) would indicate that problems of declining sexual potency affect at least 19 million men. By 2010, the male menopause population would increase by 50 percent.

This gradual change in sexual response can fuel psychological problems. Once it begins, the decline of potency can trigger performance anxiety. After experiencing difficulty or being completely unable to perform sexually on one occasion a man may think of this unpleasant event during every future sexual encounter. This often uncontrollable and powerful memory can lead a man to impotence.

Most women believe it is their fault if their middle aged husbands have become impotent. As one policeman's wife told a sexologist, "If I were Marilyn Monroe, even a dead man would get an erection." Just the opposite is true, say experts. Any middle aged man with potency fears who was confronted with a Marilyn would probably turn to jelly.

The decrease in potency associated with male menopause can stem from several factors. The most common factor is impairment of the blood supply to the penis due to vascular problems. Diabetes, hypertension, smoking, and high cholesterol can contribute to male potency by effecting the blood supply to the penis. Prescription drugs can also play a role. For example, hypertension (high blood pressure) medication can vastly increase the risk of impotence. A man may have to try five different prescriptions before he finds one that does not effect his potency.

Recreational drugs such as alcohol and tobacco can also cause male sexual dysfunction. When doctors look at the tissue from patients with chronic alcoholism they find that the nerve inside the penis is killed. It is almost impossible to revive. Smoking is probably the major contributing cause of male sexual dysfunction. Smoking damages the tiny blood vessels in the penis, so they cannot enlarge to allow the substantial onrush of blood needed to create an erection.

Even if a man is perfectly healthy and does not use alcohol or tobacco he is still likely to experience a decrease in sexual potency over time. This decrease is due to the fact that testosterone levels decrease in men as they age. Testosterone levels in most men begin to taper off in their mid-50s and 60s. Testosterone stimulates sexual development, bone and muscle growth, effects a man's sense of well-being, and stirs sexual desire.

An older man's testosterone level may measure within the broad band of normalcy, 300 to 1200 nanograms per deciliter. However, he has usually experienced a decline in his available testosterone over time. As men age production of testosterone decreases and production of a protein called sex hormone binding globulin increases. Testosterone links with the protein, reducing its availability to the tissue.

Anabolic steroids can be used to fight male menopause. At the Hormonal Healthcare Center in London, Dr. Carruthers and his partner, Dr. John Moran, have pioneered hormone replacement therapy. They have prescribed testosterone to several hundred men over the past few years.

Typically, a patient is given an implant of pellets that release testosterone continuously over a period of six months. When the effects wear off another implant is administered. "The success rate with testosterone implants is quite high," Carruthers says. Other doctors worry about the side effects that steroids may cause. Such as testicular atrophy and accelerated prostate cancer growth. As a result, testosterone replacement therapy is not widely available.

At the present time several doctors are experimenting with the use of anabolic steroids to treat male menopause. If these experiments go well anabolic steroids may soon be more widely produced and available.

Alternative methods of administration have been used to increase the effectiveness of anabolic steroids. In addition to the oral and parenteral(by injection) methods that have been discussed thus far, anabolic steroids can also be administered through subcutaneous implantation of silastic capsules or pellets, oral administration in micro particulate form, transdermal application, via rectal suppositories, and via nasal drops.

Subcutaneous implantation of testosterone pellet implant is a method of administering testosterone that many people are unaware of. Testosterone pellet implants are made by melting crystalline steroid and molding it into a cylindrical shape. Organon (Aust) Pty Ltd., a company based in Sydney Australia, manufactures 100 mg and 200 mg testosterone pellet implants. The implants have a cylindrical shape with a diameter of 4.5 mm and lengths of 6 mm(100 mg) and 12 mm(200)mg. Testosterone pellet implants are implanted through a minor surgical procedure under local anesthetic. The lower abdominal wall is the preferred site for implantation. Testosterone pellet implants that remain effective for over a year exist. However, most of the implants that are being used currently remain effective for 4-6 months. Once the implant is in the patient does not have to worry about taking testosterone. Erosion of the implanted pellet's surface at an uniform rate keeps testosterone levels

19

stable. This stability helps to decrease or totally eliminate side effects that often stem from major fluctuations in testosterone levels. Libido, potency, and mood remain relatively constant.[16]

Testosterone can be incorporated into biodegradable microspheres. Testosterone loaded microspheres can provide controlled release of testosterone for several weeks or even months.[17] In one study a single intramuscular injection of testosterone incorporated into microspheres raised a hypogonadal man's, a man that lacks testes, testosterone serum levels into the normal range for 70 days.[18]

Transdermal application of anabolic steroids is also quite effective. Anabolic steroids can be absorbed through the skin. The scrotum absorbs anabolic steroids the best, about 40 times better than the forearm.[19] In order to take advantage of the scrotum's high absorption capability a transdermal therapeutic system (TTS) for application to the scrotum was developed. The TTS consists of polymeric membranes loaded with testosterone. The membranes need to be renewed on a daily basis. When attached to the scrotal skin TTS's deliver constant serum testosterone levels.[20] Constant serum testosterone levels help to reduce or completely eliminate side effects that often stem from fluctuations in testosterone levels. Transdermal application of testosterone is becoming more wide spread because it is one of the best methods for providing constant serum testosterone levels. Accidental person to person transfer of transdermally administered testosterone may occur. This is not as likely with the TTS as the TTS is self contained in a patch like polymeric membrane. However, androgenization of female partners of men using testosterone creams have been observed.[21]

Rectal application of testosterone has been used in order to avoid first passage inactivation of testosterone by the liver. Administration of a suppository containing 40 mg of testosterone results in an immediate and steep rise of serum testosterone lasting for about 4 hours. Effective testosterone serum levels for the treatment of hypogonadal men can be achieved by repeated applications.[22] Rectal application of testosterone has not become popular because patients are reluctant to use suppositories three times a day on a long term basis.

The first passage inactivation of testosterone by the liver can also be avoided by applying testosterone to the nasal mucosa.[23] Nasal testosterone application produces unreliable absorption rates and short lived elevation of testosterone levels. As a result, nasal application is hardly every used.

In order for anabolic steroids to work they must be received and processed by individual cells. Receptor sites that can recognize anabolic steroids bind to anabolic steroid molecules and allow cells to process anabolic steroids.[24] Under normal conditions skeletal muscle anabolic steroid receptor sites are saturated with naturally occurring testosterone molecules. As a result, anabolic steroid consumption, under normal conditions, has little effect on muscle growth and strength. However, exercise increases the number of unsaturated anabolic steroid receptor sites. This increases the bodies anabolic steroid processing ability which correspondingly increases the effectiveness of anabolic steroids. Anabolic steroid use must be accompanied with physical exercise in order to promote significant muscle size and strength increases. Women have more unsaturated anabolic steroid receptors than men because women have lower testosterone, a naturally occurring anabolic steroid, levels. This means that women are more sensitive to anabolic steroids.[25]

No matter how much exercising one does, there is always a point where all of the available skeletal muscle anabolic steroid receptor sites become saturated. When this point is reached higher doses of anabolic steroids will no longer lead to increased skeletal muscle growth. However, these higher doses continue to effect other areas of the body that have unsaturated anabolic steroid receptor sites. "Anabolic steroid receptors exist not only in skeletal muscle but also in other tissues throughout the body, including the prostate, heart, testes, seminiferous tubules, and probably the brain. It is the abundance of receptors in various tissues that leads to the diverse physiologic effects of anabolic steroids."[26]

2

SIDE EFFECTS

Most of the side effects that are associated with anabolic steroid use are dose related. The higher the dose the more likely it is that one will suffer from a number of possible side effects. The following table lists some of the minor side effects that anabolic steroid use can cause. Most of these side effects occur at low doses and become more intense as doses are increased. As a result, most anabolic steroid users experience some of these side effects. Many of these side effects go away after anabolic steroid use has been stopped. However, some of these side effects can be permanent.

Minor Side Effects Caused by Anabolic Steroid Use

Acne
Fluid Retention
Change in testicular size
Psychological disturbances
Penile enlargement
Abnormal liver function tests
Increased libido
Irregular hair growth
Trouble Sleeping
Increased appetite
Gynecomastia
Deepening of the voice
Increased energy

Anabolic steroid abuse can lead to psychological and physical dependence. Dependence can make it hard for people to get off of anabolic steroids even though they may be suffering from some of the negative side effects of anabolic steroids. Some of the side effects associated with anabolic steroid use are extremely serious. Unfortunately, it is hard to find accurate figures on athletes' chances of suffering from these side effects because thorough studies of anabolic steroid use at doses used by most athletes do not exist. A large portion of the medical community feels that it would be unethical to conduct such studies because it would be too dangerous for the participants. In addition, a study that involved giving healthy individuals high doses of anabolic steroids would be illegal. In the absence of such studies it is hard to predict exactly how risky it is for athletes to use anabolic steroids.

Most of the studies that have been done concentrate on individuals that were taking anabolic steroids for therapeutic reasons. Anabolic steroids are used for a variety of therapeutic purposes ranging from treating muscular dystrophy to providing hormonal replacement for hypogonadal men. Many of the side effects listed in this book were observed in patients that were taking relatively low therapeutic doses of a particular anabolic steroid.

Athletes often do a great deal of experimenting with specific aspects of anabolic steroid administration in order to determine which methods work best for them. Stacking, using more than one steroid at a time, usually an oral and an injectable, might activate more receptor sights than if only one steroid is used. In addition, when certain anabolic steroids are taken together they may increase each other's effectiveness.[27] Taking anabolic steroid in alternating or overlapping intervals in order to avoid plateauing, developing a tolerance to a particular steroid, is also common.[28] Plateauing occurs when additional doses of an anabolic steroid are administered when all of the anabolic steroid receptor sights for that steroid are saturated. Testosterone a naturally occurring steroid, is an anabolic, tissue building, hormone and cortisol is a catabolic, tissue destroying, hormone. These hormones serve to keep tissue growth under control. If the brain senses that tissue growth is needed testosterone production can be increased, cortisol production can be decreased, or testosterone production can be increased at the same time that cortisol production is being decreased. If the aim is to decrease tissue production the opposite would occur.

Anabolic steroids are powerful muscle building agents because they promote muscle growth through two effective processes. Anabolic steroids increase the speed at which new muscle sells are produced while blocking the effects of cortisol, a muscle destroying hormone. Muscle cells contain receptor sites that are designed to receive molecules with specific shapes. Anabolic steroids and cortisol have similar molecular shapes. As a result, the same receptor sites that receive anabolic steroids receive cortisol. In order for a hormone to exert its effects it must be received by a receptor site. When anabolic steroids are used the amount of anabolic hormones present in the blood stream far outweighs the amount of catabolic hormones in the blood stream. Thus, the majority of the receptor sites that can accommodate these hormones are full of molecules that produce anabolic effects. These anabolic molecules produce a two fold increase in muscle production as they keep the catabolic molecules out of the receptor sites and they increase the rate at which new muscle cells are being produced. The body's natural method for regulating muscle growth is overridden. However, there is a catch.

The body continues to produce catabolic molecules, primarily in the form of cortisol. The level of cortisol in the blood stream continues to increase because the cortisol molecules cannot be processed through receptor sites that are filled with anabolic steroid molecules. Eventually, the number of anabolic and catabolic molecules in the blood stream reach an equal level. When a receptor site frees up it has an equal chance of receiving an anabolic or catabolic molecule. Eventually, half of the receptor sites contain anabolic molecules and half of the receptor sites contain catabolic molecules. At this point further muscle growth is not possible. A plateau is reached.

A bodybuilder stuck on such a plateau may decide to increase steroid dosages in order to counteract the large build up of cortisol in the bloodstream. However, this is only a temporary solution as a new plateau would soon be reached and dosages would have to be raised to an absurd level if one wanted to continue fighting off each successive plateau. Other bodybuilders seeing that the steroids are no longer helping to build muscle and not wanting to risk taking higher and higher dosages decide to discontinue steroid use immediately. Such cold turkey stoppage of steroid use should never be done. It leads to a state known as crashing where catabolic molecules far outweigh anabolic molecules. The majority of receptor sites become filled with catabolic molecules and a large amount of muscle is lost in a short period of time. In addition, high cortisol levels are known to cause severe depression, Cushing's Syndrome, and other significant side effects. Cortisol levels can be kept under control by using the pyramid method. Taking steroids in a pyramid like pattern, moving from low daily doses at the beginning of a cycle to higher doses and then tapering doses down toward the end of the cycle can prevent excessive cortisol build up, crashing, and plateauing.[29] The idea is to make some gains and then keep them by keeping the ratio of anabolic to catabolic molecules at equal levels.

Some bodybuilder have started using drugs that fill up cortisol receptor sites, but have little direct effect on protein synthesis. Trilostane and Mitotane (sold by Idis Ltd., 51 High Street, Kingston-upon-Thames) are two of these drugs. They are known as inhibitors because they inhibit the bodies ability to process cortisol. Muscle growth results as the tissue destroying effects of cortisol can only occur when cortisol molecules are processed through receptor sites. These drugs have significant side effects which stem from cortisol build up and other chemical reactions. The pyramid method can be used to control cortisol build up, but other side effects like vertigo and vomiting are harder to control.

As the word anabolic continues to lose some of its sales power due to it being incorporated into the name of almost every worthless supplement on the market it is likely that new lines of supplements will be built up around the cortisol inhibiting/anti-catabolic process. Don't waste your money on these new supplements. The fact is that any substance that effectively inhibits cortisol would have to be a powerful drug that could not be legally sold as a supplement.

The doses of anabolic steroids that athletes take in cycles, periods of use lasting 6 to 18 weeks or more, are frequently over 100 times the therapeutic dosage. As a result, it seems logical to conclude that athletes are likely to experience more frequent and more severe side effects than patients receiving therapeutic doses under a doctor's care.

The following table lists anabolic steroid dosages that doctors recommend as therapeutic treatment for patients with various health problems. The therapeutic dosage is the dosage recommended to produce pharmacologic responses in well defined clinical conditions.

BRAND NAME (Oral)	GENERIC NAME	THERAPEUTIC DOSAGE
Methosarb	Calusterone	50 mg. po daily
Danocrine	Danazol	200 to 800 mg. po daily
Maxibolin	Ethylestrenol	4 to 8 mg. po daily
Halotestin	Fluoxymesterone	2 to 10 mg. po daily
Dianabol	Methandrostenolone USP	2.5 to 5 mg. po daily
Metandren Oreton Methyl	Methyltestosterone	5 to 40 mg. po daily
Anavar	Oxandrolone	5 to 10 mg. po daily

BRAND NAME	GENERIC NAME	THERAPEUTIC DOSAGE
(Oral)		
Anadrol-50	Oxymetholone	5 mg./kg. po daily for anemia
Winstrol	Stanozolol	6 mg. po daily
Teslac	Testolactone	250 mg. po 4x daily for breast cancer
(Parenteral (by injection))		
Drolban	Dromostanolone propionate	100 mg. im three time weekly for breast cancer
none	Methandriol	50 to 100 mg. once or twice weekly
Deca-Durabolin	Nandrolone decanoate	50 to 100 mg. im every 3 to 4 weeks
Durabolin	Nandrolone phenpropionate	25 to 50 mg. im weekly for breast cancer
Testoject-50	Testosterone	10 to 50 mg. im three times weekly
Testex	Testosterone propionate	10 to 25 mg. im every 2 to 4 weeks
Delatestryl	Testosterone enanthate	50 to 400 mg. im every 2 to 4 weeks
Depo- Testosterone	Testosterone cypionate	50 to 400 mg. im every 2 to 4 weeks[30]

Some life threatening diseases have been linked to anabolic steroid use. The fact that anabolic steroid use is known to increase one's chances of contracting these diseases will convince some people to stop or never start using anabolic steroids. However, there will always be people who continue to use anabolic steroids. Dr. John Ziegler, the man who developed the first documented analog of testosterone in the United States, Dianabol, after learning at the 1956 World Games that Russian athletes were using testosterone, made the following comment: "I honestly believe that if I'd told people back then that rat manure would make them stronger, they'd have eaten rat manure."[31]

People who use anabolic steroids should visit their doctors on a regular basis. The key to treating many of the side effects of steroid use is early intervention. Try to find a doctor who knows a great deal about anabolic steroids and let him or her know that you use steroids. The only 100% effective way of avoiding the side effects of anabolic steroids is to avoid taking anabolic steroids. However, a good doctor can offer you a significant degree of protection. In many cases a good doctor can detect the emergence of and take actions to remedy possible problems before it is too late.

People that are unwilling to go to a doctor and do not want to get off of anabolic steroids should try to monitor their condition on their own. The discussion of side effects that follows can be used as a gauge to judge the risk/benefit ratio of individual relationships with anabolic steroids. Some people may be able to control their anabolic steroid relationship. Others may find that they are falling victim to many of the side effects of anabolic steroid use. In any event, anyone that uses or is thinking of using anabolic steroids should keep in mind that anabolic steroid abuse can lead to psychological and physical dependence. As a result, some people may need professional help in order to get off of anabolic steroids.

Mild to suicidal depression
Nausea
Chills
Headaches
Dizziness
Rapid pulse rate
Elevated blood pressure
Distorted body image
Anabolic steroid craving
Diminished libido

Intake of anabolic steroids in a pyramid like pattern, moving from low daily doses at the beginning of a cycle to higher doses and then tapering doses down toward the end of the cycle was noted as an effective way of preventing plateauing. It is also an effective method for avoiding severe anabolic steroid withdrawal symptoms. When anabolic steroid use is discontinued suddenly the body goes from having an abundance of anabolic steroids circulating in the blood to having almost no anabolic steroids circulating in the blood. The testes may not resume normal testosterone production for up to six months after steroid use has been discontinued. This sudden, severe change in hormone levels can bring on all of the symptoms listed above. In addition, the extra muscle mass that was built up has virtually no anabolic steroid molecules to use for maintenance. As a result, muscle mass is lost at an alarming rate. Using the pyramid method allows for gradual changes in hormone levels on the way up and on the way down. Gradual change is much easier on the body. It gives the testes time to resume normal testosterone production and it can prevent severe withdrawal symptoms.

When severe withdrawal symptoms occur, psychotherapy and continued exercise in a drug free environment can help. A large portion of the gains made while on anabolic steroids will be lost. However, continued exercise can preserve some of these gains. Motivation to exercise may be hard to find as x-users frequently suffer from severe depression. Drugs that may be used to treat acute hyperadrenergic physiological withdrawal and psychological withdrawal depression are naloxone and alpha2-agonists such as clonidine, followed by antidepressants.[32]

Psychological Side Effects

The psychological side effects that anabolic steroid use can cause are more prevalent and can be more serious than the physical side effects. "Brain tissue contains androgen receptors that are concentrated in certain areas of the brain, such as the hypothalamus, sexual dimorphic nucleus of the pre-optic area, the bed nucleus of the stria terminalis, and the middle portion of the amygdaloid nucleus."[33]

Several psychological side effects of anabolic steroid use have been observed. These psychological changes do not occur to the same degree in all anabolic steroid users. As a general rule, the higher the dose the more likely it is that one will experience major personality changes. Psychiatrists, Pope and Katz, reported that 4 out of 33 regular steroid users experienced psychotic symptoms, and many others exhibited near-psychotic symptoms, mania, and withdrawal depression.[34] Anabolic steroid abuse can lead to: aggression, violent episodes, paranoia, depression, and hallucinations.[35] Cycling on and off of steroids can create a psychological rollercoaster that may lead to mental imbalance.

The aggressive behavior associated with anabolic steroid use can lead to longer, more intense training sessions. However, some people find that they lose their motivation to train when they stop taking anabolic steroids. In addition, anabolic steroid induced aggressive behavior, especially when combined with alcohol, often leads to "roid rage", violent outbursts that can end friendships and ruin lives. Anabolic steroid induced criminal violence and murder is a well documented phenomenon. Several court cases exist where behavioral changes, brought about by anabolic steroid use, led to criminal activities. The following describes one of these cases.

Horace K. Williams, a 23 year old anabolic steroid user, was tried in May 1988 for the brutal murder of a hitchhiker. Williams did not have a violent history and he did not have any major psychological problems. Williams started using anabolic steroids in order to improve his athletic performance. He played football in high school and after high school he got into bodybuilding. During his trial Williams described how anabolic steroids changed his behavior. In his initial stage of anabolic steroid use, 5 mg of oral Dianabol for two weeks and then 25 mg per day for the next five weeks, Williams experienced an increase in confidence, increased ability to ask women out, and a willingness to train harder. As his steroid use increased, stacking Dianabol and oxymetholone orally along with injections of testosterone cypionate, Williams became easily agitated into violent behavior, threatened people, felt special powers, and tried to get off of steroids but "was so depressed that I thought I might kill myself if I didn't get back on steroids. I felt like a whimp when I wasn't on steroids." Upon consumption of higher doses, stacking four or mores steroids in a random fashion and daily injections, Williams became obsessed with building his body, got into several fights, felt like everyone was afraid of him, turned over 15 cars, wanted to fight everybody, lost most of his friends, and couldn't control his madness. It was in this state of mind that the anabolic steroid created personality of Horace Williams picked up a hitchhiker, drove him to an empty field, undressed him, beat him to death with a board and a lead pipe, scalped him, shaved the hair off his arms and legs, hung him with a rope, and ran him over repeatedly with his vehicle.

The Williams case is extreme. However, it is not hard to fall into the trap of taking higher and higher doses of anabolic steroids. As Williams increased his consumption of anabolic steroids his body grew bigger and stronger. He was aware of his personality changes, but he had become obsessed with developing a bigger body. In addition, some of the personality changes that anabolic steroid use can cause such as increased confidence and motivation are addictive feelings that are hard to give up. To make matters worse, many people experience intense depression when they stop taking steroids. Dr. Kirk Brower, a University of Michigan psychiatrist, documented a case where a twenty four year old weight lifter felt that he needed professional help to stop taking anabolic steroids because when he tried to stop on his own he experienced suicidal depression.[36]

Increased sexual desire, libido, is another behavioral change that anabolic steroid use can cause. Anabolic steroid use can increase or decrease libido in both men and women. While anabolic steroids are being taken libido usually increases. When anabolic steroids are not being taken, at one end of a cycle or in the initial phases of permanently discontinuing steroid use, libido can fall below normal. Once anabolic steroid use has been discontinued for a significant length of time libido usually returns to pre-steroid levels. The increase in libido that steroid use can cause has the potential to drive someone who normally has a lower, more controllable libido to commit rape.

Physical Side Effects

The physical side effects that one experiences while on anabolic steroids are largely dependent on the number of anabolic steroids taken, the dosages, and the length of steroid use. Accurate numbers on these factors as they relate to the occurrence of specific side effects are hard to find. As mentioned earlier, studies aimed at finding these numbers would involve administering high doses of anabolic steroids to healthy individuals. Under current laws, this would be illegal.

Observance of patients receiving therapeutic dosages of anabolic steroids and individual case studies of athletes have revealed that anabolic steroid use can significantly increase one's chances of suffering from the physical side effects that follow. It is believed that decreasing the number of anabolic steroids used, the dosages, and the length of time anabolic steroids are used will decrease one's chances of suffering from the following side effects. In addition, avoiding anabolic steroids that contain an alkyl group in the 17 α position may decrease one's chances of suffering from some of the more serious side effects associated with anabolic steroid use. Almost all oral anabolic steroids contain an alkyl group in the 17 α position. Methenolone acetate and testosterone undecanoate are exceptions to this rule. Most injectable anabolic steroids are testosterone esters that go easier on the liver than their oral counterparts. Dr. Eberhard Nieschlag, a leading authority on anabolic steroid replacement therapy in hypogonadal men, wrote the following in reference to some of the more serious side effects that have been associated with anabolic steroid use. "The side-effects are due to the alkyl group in the 17 α position and have also been reported for other steroids with this configuration. Because of the side-effects methyltestosterone (and other anabolic steroids with similar configurations) should no longer be used therapeutically, in particular since effective alternatives are available. The German Endocrine Society declared methyltestosterone obsolete in 1981 and the German Federal Health authority ruled that methyltestosterone should be withdrawn form the market. In other countries, however, methyltestosterone is still in use, a practice which should be terminated."[37]

Anabolic steroids (primarily oral anabolic steroids) have been linked to the development of liver cancer.[38] Treatment for liver cancer, in some cases, may be as simple as discontinuing anabolic steroid use. However, depending upon how far the cancer has developed, other treatments may be required. One study found that liver tumors, although rare among men, occur in 1-3% of men receiving oral anabolic steroids with a latency period of 2-30 years.[39] Oral anabolic steroids have also been linked to the formation of blood filled cysts in the liver although the relative risk is unknown.

Liver damage is usually caused by oral steroids. However, injectable steroids have also been linked to liver problems, including liver tumors.[40] Anabolic steroids limit the function of liver cells that are designed to extract bile, a yellow liquid that aids in digestion, from the blood.[41] This can lead to jaundice, an abnormal body condition caused by an increase of bile pigments in the blood and characterized by yellow coloration of the whites of the eyes and or skin. High levels of bile makes blood toxic. This can lead to cell death and abnormal functioning of the liver. Once the liver begins to malfunction a variety of conditions may arise. The liver may no longer produce some of the clotting factors of the blood. This can result in prolonged nose bleeds and easy bruising. The liver also serves to deactivate estrogens, female hormones. If the liver fails to do this gynecomastia, female breast development, may occur.

The development of gynecomastia due to anabolic steroid use is not completely understood. However, it has been hypothesized that in addition to stemming from a weak lever gynecomastia may also occur in the following ways. Anabolic steroids block the release of hormones that stimulate the testes. This leads to testicular atrophy. The testes become dormant and decrease in size. They no longer produce the proper levels of testosterone or sperm. Testosterone production sinks to such a low level that naturally occurring female hormones, in the absence of proper testosterone levels and synthetic anabolic steroids, start to dominate. Anabolic steroid users frequently cycle on and off of the drug. Testosterone and anabolic steroid levels can be extremely low at the point of the cycle where the testes are atrophied and anabolic steroids are not being taken. This may lead to gynecomastia. This does not mean that continual intake of anabolic steroids will prevent gynecomastia, as gynecomastia may also stem from a weak liver. It is most likely that gynecomastia occurs due to the peripheral conversion of anabolic steroids to estrogens, or conversion by the mammary tissue itself. Some anabolic steroids, such as mesterolone, fluoxymesterolone, and dihydrotestosterone cannot be converted to estrogen. The progression of gynecomastia can be stopped by discontinuing the use of the suspected drug. Regression to the point of pre-steroid use may occur. Dihydrotestosterone[42] and the estrogen receptor blockers, clomiphene(Clomid) and tamoxifen[43] (Nolvadex), have been used to treat gynecomastia and appear to have some effect if used in the early stages of the disease. In some cases surgery may be the only way to get rid of gynecomastia. The surgical procedure for treating gynecomastia has been improved in recent years. The offensive tissue is removed through liposuction and scaring is minimal.

Anabolic steroids can cause men to lactate, produce milk. Men naturally have all the proper breast components to produce milk. Highly androgenic steroids that aromatize to estrogen set off chemical reactions that cause some men to lactate. This is a rare side effect of steroid use, but it does happen. Lactation usually occurs when severe gynecomastia is present. Im most cases, removing a large percentage of receptor tissue stops lactation. However, if the individual is highly sensitive receptor tissue removal may not be enough. Sensitivity to aromatization varies from individual to individual. Cases have been reported where athletes continued to lactate for months after stopping testosterone suspension use.10 mg a day of an anti-estrogen like Nolvadex is enough to prevent lactation in most sensitive individuals. Proviron and Teslac are also effective at preventing estrogen build up.

Sperm counts, due to testicular atrophy, the testes shrinking and becoming dormant, may reach an infertile level. In most cases, once anabolic steroid use has been discontinued, the testes eventually resume normal production and both testosterone and sperm levels return to normal within 6 months. However, case reports where testicular production did not return to pre-drug rates have been recorded.[44] This suggests that infertility is a possible result of anabolic steroid use. However, these case reports leave out important information, such as whether or not the subjects permanently discontinued steroid use. As a result, it can not be conclusively stated that permanent infertility is a possible side effect of anabolic steroid use. The World Health Organization, WHO, has conducted studies aimed at evaluating the possibility of using anabolic steroids as a form of male contraception. WHO studies have shown that testosterone enanthate is a safe contraceptive once azoospermia has been achieved. However, only 2/3 of the men in a WHO study involving 240 couples developed azoospermia.[45] At the conclusion of the study all of the participants' sperm counts returned to pre-steroid levels.

A case of Wilm's tumor in an adult male steroid user has been reported.[46] Wilm's tumor is a kidney tumor that is almost exclusively limited to children. Thus, when a doctor comes across an adult that has been taking anabolic steroids and has Wilm's tumor it is logical for the doctor to hypothesize that the tumor is in some way related to steroid use. However, Wilm's tumor has also been observed in adult men that have never used steroids. As a result, Wilm's tumor can not be conclusively linked to anabolic steroid use. "In rodents, androgens stimulate kidney growth. However, there is no apparent human analogy to this effect and, apart from stimulating erythropoietin secretion, androgens do not appear to have important effects on the human kidney."[47] Erythropoietin is a natural hormone produced by the kidneys that increases the body's oxygen carrying capacity by stimulating bone marrow to increase production of red blood cells. Increased oxygen carrying capacity usually leads to an increase in aerobic endurance. Many long distance runners and other endurance athletes take anabolic steroids hoping to increase their aerobic endurance. However, it has not been proven that anabolic steroids increase erythropoietin secretion to a high enough level to produce significant increases in aerobic endurance.

Anabolic steroids cause salt and water retention by limiting the liver's ability to deactivate Cortisol, a naturally occurring hormone. Some of the size and weight gained through the use of anabolic steroids is a direct result of salt and water retention. Salt and water retention can lead to high blood pressure and edema, excessive fluid in body cavities or tissues. This can lead to heart disease. Hypercortisolemia, high cortisol levels, may cause some of the behavioral changes, ranging from depression to psychotic behavior, associated with anabolic steroid use.

Anabolic steroid use may lead to heart disease. Anabolic steroids are known to significantly alter lipoprotein levels.[48] Lipoprotein, cholesterol, levels may reach a dangerous point. The link between heart attacks and high cholesterol levels is well established. An individual who has a family history of heart attacks may suffer from a heart attack earlier, due to anabolic steroid use, than he would have purely as a result of his genealogy. Cholesterol levels usually return to normal approximately one month after steroid use has been discontinued. Studies have shown that oral anabolic steroids have a greater effect on cholesterol levels than injectable anabolic steroids.[49]

There is evidence that suggest that prostate enlargement and prostate cancer can be caused by anabolic steroid use. The prostate is a target tissue for anabolic steroids. Anabolic steroids make established cases of prostate cancer worse. In fact, treatment for prostate cancer usually involves reducing or completely blocking testosterone secretion. There is one documented case report that describes the development of prostate cancer in a 40 year old bodybuilder.[50] 40 is a young age to develop prostate cancer. However, prostate cancer has not been conclusively proven to stem from anabolic steroid use. As anabolic steroid users grow older we will be able to get a better idea of the relationship between anabolic steroids and the development of prostate cancer.

Anabolic steroids can cause acne. The androgenic, masculinizing effects of anabolic steroids, can cause an increase in oil production by the sebaceous glands of the skin.[51] White heads, zits, can develop anywhere on the body. Acne usually subsides once steroid use has been discontinued.

Anabolic steroid use can increase hair growth on the face, chest, back, and lower abdomen. It is speculated that anabolic steroids can speed up male pattern baldness in people that are genetically predisposed to this condition. Male pattern baldness as a result of anabolic steroid use has not been studied very thoroughly. However, it is known that castration can prevent or arrest baldness in men, and treatment of castrated men with anabolic steroids again permits scalp hair loss.[52]

Steroids permit cartilage growth. Parts of the nose, ears, and larynx are made of cartilage. Ear growth is not very noticeable. The nose growth is more noticeable on women than men. Although rare, steroids cause the cartilage surrounding the outer larynx to thicken and take on the appearance of the male's Adam's Apple in some women. Cartilage growth is irreversible. In some instance, as with nose jobs, the offensive cartilage can be removed through plastic surgery.

Tendon injury is another dangerous side effect that can result from anabolic steroid use. Some people believe that the aggressive attitude that can result from steroid use encourages people to attempt lifts that are too heavy and to continue working out when they should be resting. Such behavior can lead to tendon rupture. Tendon rupture, the detachment of a tendon from the bone, is extremely painful. When a tendon ruptures the muscle that it is attached to roles up into a ball and surgery is required to repair the injury. Tendon rupture can end an athlete's career. Some evidence suggests that continued use of steroids can cause tendons to lose their elasticity and thus increase one's chance of rupturing a tendon.

Certain individuals may have an allergic reaction to anabolic steroids. Anaphylactic shock occurs in a relatively small portion of the population. However, when it happens immediate medical attention is required in order to prevent death. Septic shock, caused by contamination of the drug or syringe, is also a possible side effect of anabolic steroid use. Syringes can get contaminated easily in a gym bag and drugs bought on the black-market are frequently contaminated. Both of these types of shock can cause ear throbbing, palpitations, difficulty breathing, and itching. Medical treatment can alleviate these symptoms.

Most of the side effects that have been discussed thus far can effect adult males, adult females, and adolescents. Obviously, adult women and female adolescents can't suffer from testicular atrophy or prostate cancer. However, they are capable of contracting all of the other side effects that have been discussed thus far. Furthermore, adult women and adolescents are susceptible to some side effects that do not occur in the adult male.

The negative side effect potential of anabolic steroids is greatest for the adolescent female. Anabolic steroids can stunt growth in both female and male adolescents. When a female or male adolescent takes anabolic steroids premature epiphyseal closure can occur. The epiphyses is the part of the bone where new growth occurs. Once it is closed growth is permanently stopped. Discontinuing steroid use will not cause bone growth to resume. As a result, the adolescent athlete that had hoped to gain size by taking anabolic steroids actually ends up limiting his or her growth. Most bones stop growing when they are about twenty two years old. However, some bones, like the xiphoid, the end tip of the sternum, grow for thirty years or more.[53] Premature stoppage of bone growth can lead to a distorted body that has not and never will reach full growth potential. Adolescent females along with adult females suffer further side effects, such as loss of or irregularities in menstruation, that are not found among adolescent and adult males.

Anabolic steroids are patterned after testosterone, a naturally occurring male hormone. Testosterone is responsible for many of the characteristics that make men men and thus make men different from women. Testosterone occurs naturally in women. However, the average woman has approximately 100 times less testosterone than the average man.[54] When a female takes anabolic steroids she is taking a drug that tricks her body into thinking that she is a man. Consumption of anabolic steroids by females can lead to carcinoma of the breast, masculinization of the fetus, hirsutism (hair growth on various areas of the body including the growth of mustaches and beards), male pattern baldness, deepening of the voice, and clitoral enlargement.[55] "These changes are usually irreversible even after prompt discontinuance of therapy and are not prevented by concomitant usage of estrogens."[56] These changes are likely to occur in all females that take anabolic steroids. The depth and permanence of these changes is likely to be most severe in the adolescent female. Anti androgens such as cyproterone acetate are used for treatment of acne and hirsutism in women.[57] Prolonged consumption of anabolic steroids by females is similar to a sex change operation. In fact, anabolic steroids are given to females that have sex change operations.

Anabolic steroids speed up bone growth before stopping bone growth through epiphyseal closure. Thus, if an individual started taking steroids just prior to the time that epiphyseal closure was going to occur naturally he could end up taller than he would have been other wise. Small doses of anavar do not cause bone closure. In fact, pediatricians have used anavar to increase height in teenagers. The amount of anavar that will increase height without causing bone closure varies from individual to individual and can only be determined by an experienced doctor. Steroids can cause bones that continue to grow into the late 20's and early 30's to undergo noticeable accelerated growth before causing bone closure. Bone growth in the chin and jaw are good examples of this. The effect is usually more noticeable in women who often end up with a sharp jaw line that ends in an extremely pointy chin.

Anabolic steroid users, like all injectable drug users, have a higher than normal chance of catching AIDS. AIDS is spread through heterosexual sex, homosexual sex, and needle sharing. The chances of catching AIDS when using injectable drugs can be greatly reduced by avoiding the sharing of needles. Many people do not know that they have AIDS until they are tested. In addition, you can not tell if some one has AIDS just by looking at them.

Hypodermic needle use can cause several other negative side effects. Most people are afraid and reluctant to have a needle stuck into their body. Self administration is often more mentally taxing than having a doctor do the injection. In addition, using needles does cause a certain amount of pain. The smaller the needle the less the pain. In fact, when done properly, an injection with a small sharp needle can be relatively painless.

Needles intended for human use are classified by size, diameter, with a number between 18 and 28. The larger the number, the smaller the needle. Most injectable steroids are oil base. It is not possible to draw the oil through an extremely small needle. However, once in the syringe oil base steroid can be injected through almost any size needle. This is because a very small amount of suction is used to draw liquids into the syringe. A much larger amount of force is available for pushing the oil back out through the needle. As a result, many frequent injectors draw the steroid in through a large needle and then put a small needle on the syringe before injecting. Needles can be purchased independently from the syringe. The needles are then screwed or snapped on to the syringe.

In addition to decreasing pain, using a smaller needle help to prevent the build up of scar tissue. Repeated injections, even with a small needle, can cause scar tissue to develop at the injection sight. The scar tissue feels like a small lump under the skin. Large needles produce larger areas of scaring than small needles. Excessive scaring in muscle tissue can weaken the muscle. Scaring also causes problems with future injections as scar tissue is tough and needles do not pass through it easily. Once scaring develops a new injection sight must be used. Scar tissue is has low blood flow. As a result, it does not effectively facilitate absorption of the drug.

Dirty needles can cause infections. If needles must be reused sanitary practice is to draw and expel bleach or isopropyl alcohol three to four times after each use. New, sterile insulin needles can be purchased in most states without a prescription.

As mentioned earlier, oral anabolic steroids have been linked to more side effects than injectable anabolic steroids. In general, it is believed that injectable anabolic steroids are safer than oral anabolic steroids. In fact, injectable anabolic steroids have been used and studied for many years by the World Health Organization for use in male contraception. However, injectable anabolic steroids have been linked to stroke, liver cancer, and prostate cancer. A few cases have been reported where the use of extremely high doses of oral and or injectable anabolic steroids led to strokes. Two of these cases involved bodybuilders that were using extremely high doses of injectable anabolic steroids.[58]

Many athletes resort to polypharmacy. Polypharmacy consist of taking other drugs in conjunction with anabolic steroids. Athletes do this for a variety of reasons including: attempting to avoid some of the side effects of steroid use, to pass drug tests, and to prepare for competition. Human chorionic gonadotropin can be used to prevent testicular atrophy, anti-estrogens like tamoxifen(Nolvadex) and clomiphene(Clomid) can be used to decrease the estrogen effects of anabolic steroids, and amphetamines and diuretics can be used to reduce body weight in order to meet the required weight for competition or to produce an extremely cut look. Lasix, a diuretic, was recently implicated in the death of a top bodybuilder, Mohammed Benaziza. Benaziza was taking the drug while drinking extremely small amounts of water in order to get as cut as possible for a show. He won the show, but he died a few hours latter. Corticosteroids are locally injected into inflamed joints in order to speed up the healing process. Corticosteroids should not be confused with anabolic steroids. Corticosteroids have anti-inflammatory, catabolic, effects. They break tissue down. They will not build muscle. Cortisone acetate (Cortone), hydrocortisone, prednisone, methylprednisolone (Medrol and Depo-Medrol), triamcinolone (Aristocort), dexamethasone (Decadron), and betamethasone (Celestone) are commonly used corticosteroids.[59] Excessive use of corticosteroids can lead to weakened tissue and degenerative arthritis in the joints involved. Athletes often become so obsessed with winning that they will put any drug that they think will increase their performance into their bodies. Mixing drugs, even under a doctors care, can be extremely dangerous. The athlete that tries to conduct polypharmacy on himself is playing a dangerous game that could easily result in death.

3

ANABOLIC STEROIDS AND THE LAW

The Steroid Trafficking Act of 1990 reclassified anabolic steroids as schedule III controlled substances. This put anabolic steroids in the same category as some codeine preparations, less potent amphetamines, and some barbiturates. The justification for reclassifying anabolic steroids as schedule III controlled substances is that anabolic steroids possess major psychoactive properties and have significant abuse potential. The maximum penalties for the illegal manufacturing or distribution of anabolic steroids, in other words for being an anabolic steroid dealer, are 5 years in prison, a $15,000 fine, and 2 years probation. For a second offense the maximum penalties are 10 years in prison, a $30,000 fine, and 4 years probation. Schedule III drugs are reported to have a lower abuse potential than schedule I and II drugs. Schedule I drugs include heroin, marijuana, LSD, and mescaline. The maximum penalty for illegal manufacturing or distribution of schedule I drugs is 15 years in prison, a $25,000 fine, and 3 years probation. Schedule II drugs include morphine, opium, cocaine, and codeine. They carry the same penalties as schedule I drugs. The primary difference between schedule I and schedule II drugs is that schedule II drugs have a medical use.

The government is more concerned with the manufacturing and distribution of illegal drugs than with illegal possession. As a result, dealers and manufactures receive stiffer penalties than users. Under current laws the maximum penalties for dealers and manufacturers, listed above, are the same as the maximum penalties for users. However, users rarely, if ever, receive anywhere close to these maximum penalties. The main way users get into deep trouble is when they start dealing. Dealing, even among a small group of close friends, can significantly increase the penalties that one is likely to receive. In some instances small time dealers are given the chance to rat on their suppliers in exchange for decreased sentences. However, this does not happen in all cases and those that squeal frequently fall victim to crimes committed by suppliers that are seeking retribution. Once one is caught he is at the mercy of the judicial system.

There is no doubt that help should be made available to all the people that have become involved with anabolic steroids. However, as with the case of most drugs, the powers that be decided to take the traditional route, attempting to limit the manufacturing and distribution of the drug. Reclassifying anabolic steroids as schedule III drugs will not help the anabolic steroid user and it will not stop anabolic steroid use among the general public. Drugs such as marijuana and LSD have been subjected to stricter regulations than schedule III drugs for many years. Marijuana and LSD are still big business despite the risks involved with dealing and manufacturing these drugs. Furthermore, anabolic steroids are produced in mass quantities by companies inside and outside the United States. Even if anabolic steroids had been reclassified as schedule I or II drugs, which would have placed manufacturing quotas on the production of anabolic steroids within the United States, there would still be mass quantities of anabolic steroids produced outside the United States that could be smuggled in.

Anabolic steroids can be purchased legally, without a prescription, in many Latin American and some European countries. Spain, Yugoslavia, Hungary, and Mexico are some of these countries. Recently, many Mexican pharmacies located near the border have started requiring prescriptions for anabolic steroids. However, obtaining a prescription is usually quite easy. One walks into a doctor's office, often located near the pharmacy and advertising that they sell prescriptions, says what medication one wants the prescription for and pays some money. Most pharmacies located farther into Mexico do not require prescriptions for anabolic steroids. These countries, no matter how tight the regulations regarding the manufacturing and distribution of anabolic steroids within the United States, assure that anabolic steroids will always be available on the black-market in the United states. These countries provide easy product access for smugglers while laws restricting anabolic steroids make anabolic steroid smuggling extremely lucrative.

The reclassification of anabolic steroids as schedule III drugs will make the black-market more dangerous, but it will not solve the anabolic steroid problem. It is estimated that up to 90% of the anabolic steroids on the black-market are contaminated or consist of other substances besides anabolic steroids. The only way to be sure that a product purchased on the black-market is genuine is to have it analyzed in a qualified lab. Making it more difficult to obtain genuine anabolic steroids while steroid demand remains high has led to an increase in the sale of anabolic steroid counterfeits.

The criminal justice system has repeatedly proven that it is unable to deal with the drug problem. Increasing the penalties for manufacturing and distributing illegal drugs has clogged our prisons and cost the tax payers millions of dollars. Yet we are left with a drug problem that is worse than ever. It is quite clear that law enforcement is not able to effectively enforce the drug laws. Instead of changing the laws the government chooses to continue fighting a losing battle with ineffective weapons. The higher ups in government refuse to recognize that their polices perpetuate the problem by maintaining the existence of a lucrative drug trade. They refuse to face the fact that they are not and never will be able to stop the manufacturing, smuggling, dealing, and use of illegal drugs. Furthermore, they do not want to believe that they make drug use more dangerous by making it illegal. There is no quality control on the black-market. Users can not be sure that what they are taking is pure.

Bodybuilders often end up using anabolic steroids that were produced for veterinarian uses. Veterinarian steroids are sold on the balckmarket. Some bodybuilders obtain veterinarian steroids through other sources. A few years ago it was relatively easy for athletes to find doctors that were willing to prescribe and monitor their use of anabolic steroids. However, The Anabolic Steroid Control Act of 1990 made it much more risky for doctors to help patients that wanted to use steroids for athletic and or cosmetic purposes. The Anabolic Steroid Control act of 1990 reclassified anabolic steroids as schedule III controlled substances. This means that a doctor can be sentenced to up to 5 years in prison and forced to pay up to a $250,000 fine for providing athletes with steroids. Some doctors continue to supply athletes with steroids, but it is much more difficult for the recreational athlete to find such doctors now than it was prior to the passage of The Anabolic Steroid Control Act of 1990.

This turn of events, while no doubt viewed as a victory by those politicians who supported The Anabolic Steroid Control Act of 1990, has served to make steroid use more dangerous than it needs to be. A large number of people are presently using and will continue to use steroids despite the recently passed legislation. The only difference is that these people are now forced to use suspect black market steroids that may be contaminated, counterfeits, or drugs other than steroids. I have heard of one case where an athlete purchased haldol decanoate, a powerful depressant, mistakenly thinking that it was nandrolone decanoate, an anabolic steroid, due to the fact that the names of both drugs include the word decanoate. If this athlete had sought a doctor's advice prior to use of the purchased drug this incidence could have been easily avoided. Most doctors will no longer prescribe steroids for athletic purposes. However, many doctors are willing to monitor and advise patients that are using steroids obtained from other sources.

Some athletes have turned to veterinarians in hopes of obtaining the steroids that they so strongly desire. Most of the anabolic steroid products that veterinarians dispense were reclassified as schedule III drugs in The Anabolic Steroid Control Act of 1990. However, veterinarians are not as aware of this legislation as are regular doctors. This is primarily due to the fact that veterinarians prescribe drugs for animals. Anabolic steroid regulations are further confused for the veterinarian due to the fact that anabolic steroid products that are intended for administration through implants for cattle or other nonhuman species and have been approved by the FDA for this purpose are excluded from scheduling as controlled substances. Some bodybuilders have taken to chopping up Finaplix implants and injecting them. This is a dangerous practice as there is no sterility when this is done. Anything that is going to be injected into the body should be sealed in sterile plastic or glass containers. It does not matter how carefully one tries to keep conditions sterile. The fact is that implants can be subjected to all kinds of contaminants when being stored in veterinary warehouses. In addition to implants, The Secretary of Health and Human Services also may exempt other products from regulation based on their concentration, mixture, or delivery system, provided that they have no considerable potential for abuse.

Many of the anabolic steroid products that veterinarians can prescribe are extremely similar to anabolic steroids that regular doctors would prescribe for human patients (this is why these products fall under schedule III regulations). Winstrol-V, Equipoise, and Laurabolin are some of the least dangerous steroids that veterinarians prescribe. Athletes, have come up with a way of obtaining steroids from veterinarians. They go to a number of veterinarians and try to obtain steroids by offering plausible animal justifications for the drugs. One of the most common reasons that pets are prescribed steroids is castration. Castrated pets often lose energy quickly and are no longer as active or as healthy as they once were. Steroids can be used to boost a castrated pet's energy level. Desperate bodybuilders try to obtain relatively small amounts of steroids, amounts not generally associated with abuse, from a number of veterinarians in order to conceal their true motives.

Bodybuilders also use other veterinarian products to enhance their physique. Many of these products can be dangerous as they often contain animal hormones. One such veterinary product contains a combination of HCG, Human Chorionic Gonadotropin, and pregnant mare serum gonadotropin. HCG is a protein hormone that contains polypeptide contaminants. The immune system often reacts violently against foreign proteins even when they are from human origin. Animal gonadotropins do not contain exactly the same amino acid sequences as human gona-

49

dotropins. As a result, it is much more likely that the human body will recognize animal gonadotropins as foreign. It is hard to say what, if anything, a person could catch by taking pregnant mare serum gonadotropin as it is not intended for human consumption. It is possible that one could develop anaphylactic shock or serum sickness from it.

The use of veterinarian products by humans often carries additional risk. This makes sense as veterinarian products are not intended for consumption by humans. Veterinarian products are frequently held to lower quality control standards than drugs intended for use by people. In addition, many of the ingredients in veterinarian products are from animal origins and are in doses unsuitable for people.

Making anabolic steroids illegal has created and promoted hypocrisy in the world of professional bodybuilding. Certain bodybuilding magazines, knowing that they can not make money by selling anabolic steroids because selling anabolic steroids is illegal, fill their pages with pictures of steroid monsters and promote the idea that supplements made these monsters big. Millions of readers spend millions of dollars on these supplements, the majority of which are useless, and the owners of the magazines get rich. Anyone that gets into bodybuilding for a significant amount of time soon learns that all of the top bodybuilders take steroids. Then the pictures of professional bodybuilders, whether they are in supplement ads or not, start to serve as advertisements for anabolic steroids. Thus, all bodybuilding magazines, due to the fact that they promote anabolic steroid use, should be required to run comprehensive, accurate articles on anabolic steroids. Some of the better bodybuilding magazines do this, but many bodybuilding magazines continue to hide and or cloud the facts for monetary purposes.

Huge bodybuilders full of steroids and other drugs are promoted as visions of health. When the fact is, especially around contest time, that these bodybuilders are flirting with death in order to look the way they do. Even death can not pierce monetary motives. Ambulances should be standing by at bodybuilding competitions. Everyone knows that many of the competitors have fasted and or taken diuretics in order to get that extremely cut look that is in demand. Professional bodybuilders have to go to extreme measures to achieve the look promoted by bodybuilding magazines that fund many bodybuilding contests. It is not uncommon to take a walk backstage and see competitors puking their guts out minutes before competition. The promoters know this, but the promoters also know how to sell. They know that if they provide ambulances and a significant number of qualified doctors the media will start reporting the true dangers involved with professional bodybuilding. The image of health would go down the drain and the general public would realize that professional bodybuilders flirt with death in order to win money at contests organized by people that promote bodybuilders as the epitome of health. This trend is likely to continue as long as anabolic steroids remain illegal.

Increasing the regulations and restrictions involving drugs is not a solution. It would be ideal if we could stop the flow of illegal drugs into and around the United States. However, this is not an ideal world. We have tried this approach for several decades and it has failed miserably. It has created and perpetuated a lucrative drug trade that is extremely violent. A new approach must be taken. Regulations and restrictions regarding drugs should be decreased and monies allotted to education should be increased several fold.

When the topic of legalizing drugs is brought up many people get extremely frustrated. Some people picture hard drugs being sold in every supermarket and candy story to people of all ages. However, most people that support legalization do not support such a scenario. Restrictions would still exist under legalization. Alcohol is a legal drug however there are restrictions on age and consumption when driving. Furthermore, restrictions have been placed on obtaining licenses to sell alcohol. Under legalization most drugs would be subject to far more regulation than alcohol. Some drugs might even remain illegal. Lessening the restrictions on drugs is the only way that the United States will be able to control the drug problem. Legalization has the potential to put an end to the black-market. If drugs were legalized drug dealing would not be lucrative. This would significantly reduced drug related crime. Furthermore, the legal sale of drugs could be taxed. This additional tax revenue would generate millions of dollars that could be used to improve the programs and information available for drug users and to pay off the national deficit. In addition, additional monies would be saved as drug related crime would be reduced.

Countries like Holland, where most drugs are legal, have much less of a drug problem than the United States does. The U.S. can study the systems of such countries and adopt their proven methods. How many years must go by before people realize that the current polices are not working. Making drugs illegal makes drug use far more dangerous and it fuels the majority of crime in our country. Drug dealing is one of the most appealing jobs for inner city youth because it is extremely profitable. Legalization would take this profit away. Drug abuse would occur under legalization. However, it would not be as rampant as it is now. Education and drug user facilities, fueled by the extra tax revenue legalization would create, would be more wide spread and better equipped to deal with drug abuse. People would have accurate information on the safest ways to use drugs and the medical community could conduct thorough studies on anabolic steroids and other drugs. The bottom line is that people are going to take drugs whether they are illegal or legal. If drugs were legal we could generate a significant amount of new tax dollars and we could make drug use safer and less wide spread.

4

ANABOLIC STEROID DETECTION

Anabolic steroid drug testing is conducted in many sports. On a few occasions famous athletes have tested positive for anabolic steroids. However, most athletes pass anabolic steroid drug tests. A little over 1% of the athletes tested in 1990 tested positive. This is an extremely low number considering the fact that 15-40% of athletes use anabolic steroids. (Among certain groups of athletes, such as bodybuilders and powerlifters the rate of steroid use is much higher.) Several factors contribute to the low number of positive tests. Tests used to detect anabolic steroids have certain limitations. Furthermore, athletes and other individuals, including doctors, involved with the lucrative world of sport have come up with ways of passing anabolic steroid drug tests.

Athletes are willing to do extraordinary things in order to pass drug tests. Some of these things are more painful and less effective than others. Immediately prior to the 1988 Olympics three Canadian weight lifters were informed that they were going to have to take a surprise drug test. In a last minute desperate attempt to pass the test the three athletes had clean urine forced into their bladders through the catheter.[60] One of the athletes had to go through this extremely painful process twice because he could not hold in the urine the first time. Despite their effort, all three athletes failed to pass the test. As noted this situation was complicated by the fact that the test was unexpected. Most athletes know in advance if they are going to be subjected to drug tests. This gives them time to clean out their systems. There are limits to how long a particular anabolic steroid can be detected by urine based drug testing after use of that steroid has been discontinued. Deca-Durabolin, Nandrolone decanoate, is the anabolic steroid that has the longest detection time, a few months. Anavar, Oxandrolone, can only be detected for a few days.[61]

Gas chromatography-mass spectrometry is the mandated technique for anabolic steroid testing. Maps of previously determined anabolic steroid metabolites are used to detect anabolic steroid metabolites in urine. This test is one of the most accurate tests available in modern medicine. However, it has its limitations.

Twenty seven kinds of anabolic steroids are currently classified as schedule III controlled substances. These include: boldenone, chlorotestosterone, clostebol, dehydrochlormethyltestosterone, drostanolone, dihydrotestosterone, ethylestrenol, fluoxymesterone, formobulone, mesterolone, methandienone, methandranone, methandrostenolone, methandriol, methenolone, methyltestosterone, mibolerone, nandrolone, norethandrolone, oxandrolone, oxymetholone, oxymesterone, stanolone, stanozolol, testolactone, testosterone, trenbolone, and "any drug that is chemically and pharmacologically related to the male hormone testosterone and that promotes or purports to promote muscle growth".[62] Some of these anabolic steroids do not metabolize to a unique metabolite that can be found in urine. This means that gas chromatography-mass spectrometry can not detect all existing kinds of anabolic steroids. Athletes can pass drug tests by using anabolic steroids for which there are no unique urine metabolites.

Testosterone poses an unique problem when it comes to drug tests. People naturally possess a certain level of testosterone. As a result, scientists had to come up with an accurate way of measuring naturally occurring testosterone levels. Scientists decided to use the ratio of testosterone to its epimer, epitestosterone (its chemical mirror image also produced by the testes) as the criteria for determining illegal testosterone use.[63] The naturally occurring ratio of testosterone to epitestosterone was set at 1:1. Due to the possibility of naturally occurring fluctuations in this ratio the testosterone to epitestosterone ratio for determining illegal testosterone use was set at 6:1. This means that an athlete can have over 5 times the normal testosterone level and still pass the test. Furthermore, athletes have known for some time that injecting epitestosterone parenterally or into the urinary bladder itself can prevent the detection of exogenous testosterone.[64] The ease with which the test for exogenous testosterone can be passed has encouraged many women, that are subject to drug tests, to start using testosterone instead of other less androgenic synthetic anabolic steroids like Oxandrolone (Anavar) and Stanozolol (Winstrol).

Certain drugs can be used to prevent the detection of anabolic steroids. One of these drugs, Probenecid, is used in the prophylactic treatment of gout.[65] The drug is taken at times when random drug testing is likely to occur. The International Olympic Committee has identified Probenecid and added it to the list of banned substances. However, there is no doubt that there are other masking agents that the IOC. has yet to identify. Furthermore, some masking agents that can not be detected exist. Ethacrynic acid, a diuretic that can dilute urine enough to make recent anabolic steroid use undetectable, is very difficult, if not impossible, to detect.[66]

Passing drug tests is extremely important to many people. For an athlete passing a drug test can be the difference between a gold medal and no medal. For millions of other people, passing a drug tests can be the difference between keeping a job and losing a job. As a result, there is a great demand for masking agents, products that allow people that use drugs to pass drug tests. Vince Bovino, a Southern California bodybuilder and entrepreneur recognized this demand and developed a product called Defend that he claims can foil any drug test. Analysis of Defend has revealed that it is merely glucose, a substance that has no know masking properties There are, undoubtedly, many other con-artists out their trying to pull the same scam.

Some athletes have turned to anabolic agents that can not be detected in order to pass drug tests. Human growth hormone, erythropoietin, somatomedin-C, leutenizing hormone releasing hormone, and gonadotropin releasing hormone can not be detected through current drug testing procedures. Other anabolic agents like orotic acid, in addition to being undetectable, have not yet been banned.

One of the major problems with drug testing is that it is expensive. It cost abut $150 to test a single urine specimen for anabolic steroids. Most of the labs that take samples of urine for anabolic steroid testing send these samples to one of the few labs that have been approved to detect anabolic steroids in urine. At present, the demand for test is greater than the supply of testing facilities. As a result, there is a large back log of samples that need to be tested. This factor, coupled with the expenses involved with testing, makes it difficult to obtain high quality test for anabolic steroids. Even those organizations that have money and resources limit their testing. The International Olympic Committee does not test every single athlete that competes in the Olympics. This would be too expensive. Furthermore, issues of privacy are deeply intertwined with drug testing. Many people believe that drug testing violates one's right to privacy. The supreme court has ruled that drug testing is legal under certain circumstances. However, significant bias against random, unannounced testing exists. Many people that recognize the flaws of the current drug testing program feel that random unannounced testing would solve the problem. However, as the preceding discussion indicates, this is not the case. Athletes and doctors motivated by the large amounts of money that can be made in sport have come up with effective, scientific ways of passing current drug tests. Improving drug testing procedures would not produce an unbeatable test. It would, most likely, make the process even more expensive and could further inconvenience athletes by being based on blood rather than urine. Drug testing will never remove anabolic steroids from sport.

Drug testers and drug testing agencies can be influenced by money and famous athletes. Highly accurate drug tests along with stiff penalties could lead to the expulsion of some of the world's best athletes. This might scare other athletes into discontinuing steroid use. However, the organizations and countries that back athletes have the power to influence drug testing procedures and to develop new ways of passing drug tests. As long as athletics remains lucrative corruption, both on and off the playing field, will continue.

People in power have stressed anabolic steroid testing in order to perpetuate the myth that sport is clean. They do not want people to know that the athletic performances that they are paying to see were made possible through the use of anabolic steroids. It would be great if a drug test existed that was cheap, effective, easy to administer, and impossible to fool. However, it is highly unlikely that such a test will ever be invented. The large sums of money that have been wasted on inefficient drug testing, like the large sums of money that have been wasted on attempting to enforce drug laws that are unenforceable, hurt the average citizen the most.

This money could have been put to better use if it was put into education. Our government has fallen into the pattern of catching and punishing instead of helping and supporting. As a result, an antagonistic relationship has been created. People work to find new ways of passing drug tests and to hide their drug use from the law while the government tries to catch them. Imposing restrictions on drug use has not been effective. It is costing a great deal of money, but it does little to solve the problem. Education, which can be a solution, will only be effective if trust is bestowed upon the individual citizen. This means that information regarding the use and abuse of drugs must be given to individuals in a society where drugs are under fewer restrictions. The government must trust the citizen to, with the help of proper education, handle drugs responsibly. This has been done in Holland and it has been effective. Under such circumstances the two parties could work together instead of fighting one another. The potential to make significant improvements in the drug problem at large would exist because facilities and resources could be directed towards a drug problem that had come out of the closet and no longer served to support criminals. Those people that continue to argue that drug testing and increased penalties are the solution need to wake up. These things have not worked in the past, they do not work now, and they will not work in the future. In our society the drug problem is bigger than ever. We must try something new. We must reduce the restrictions on drugs.

5

ANABOLIC STEROID EXPERIENCES

This chapter contains first hand accounts that people, including some top bodybuilders, have had with anabolic steroids and other muscle building agents. Some of the accounts were taken directly from body-builders' personal training diaries (with their full consent). Others were sent to me for publication in *Anabolic Steroid News*. *Anabolic Steroid News* is a monthly newsletter that I put out. It contains the latest information on anabolic steroids and other powerful muscle building agents. It also serves as a forum where individuals that have used anabolic steroids and other effective substances can share what they have learned. If you would like to subscribe to Anabolic Steroid News a one year subscription is $29.95 or two years for $49.95 (foreign subscribers $39.95 one year $59.95 two years). To subscribe send your name, address, check, money order, or credit card information to: Belle International-Dept. C, P.O. Box 160233, Sacramento, CA 95816.

The names of the individuals who reported the following experiences have been left out to protect their privacy. In some instance, I have responded to questions that their steroid experiences raise. The first hand experiences that individuals have had with anabolic steroids reveal valuable information that can help other bodybuilders. If you have an experience you would like to share, or a question that you would like answered please send it to the address above.

"Start Oct. 3
Body weight: 189
Flat bench: 205
Incline bench: 195
Squat: 265

Hauk squat: 295
Lat pull down to chest: 277
Seated Rows: 260
Over head triceps extensions: 95
Machine curls: 160
Standing calf raises: 455
Reverse curls: 60
Shrugs: 490
Shoulder press: 135
Up right rows: 135

Drugs: Taking Stanozolol tablets 20 mg a day plus Testosterone Propionate injections every five days starting October 4 for a total of ten injections. The tabs are 5 mg each and the injections are 1 cc each containing 100 mg. I will be taking a total of 200 tablets. The whole cycle will last about fifty days.

Body Measurements

Chest 42	Thigh 23 and 1/2
Arms 14	Calf 15
Neck 16	Forearms 12.5

October 12: I have completed my first nine days. I have already gained five pounds, but I have not noticed any real strength gains yet. I tend to become angry fairly easily but nothing that I can not control. Lately my libido has been on a rampage. I have not noticed increased acne or puffiness due to water retention. If anything, I now have better definition.

October 20: I have completed the first seventeen days of my cycle. I have been noticing significant changes in my strength, about an increase of fifteen pounds of strength per major body part and 10 pounds for smaller body parts. My overall weight is now at 198 pounds. I have been feeling a little restless lately, and feel I should be in the gym more often. I have had some problems sleeping but this is on and off and not profoundly disturbing. I have noticed that my libido is extremely high even for me, good thing I have a girlfriend. I have been noticing increases in my acne, but it seems to go away fairly fast. I have not noticed any great change in aggression, but this is only my opinion. At this point I am still taking four pills a day and an injection every five days. I should hit my peek in anther 15 days or so.

October 25: I have now taken a total of five injections. I am still taking four pills a day. My weight is now at 200 pounds but I have days where I look hard and ripped and other days where I look soft and fat, actually it looks like water retention. I have also noticed that my shoulders have not had a great strength increase and they are not as full as the rest of my muscles. This dose not make sense since my shoulders were one of my best body parts. My recovery abilities are great, my muscles never seem to be sore the next day. As far as side effects go I have noticed that my testicles have atrophied, also I seem to be losing a little bit of hair on my head and the hair on my face grows faster. On the positive side I have had no problems with acne. I feel that I can gain another nine pounds.

October 30: I have now taken a total of eight injections. When I bought my stanozolol tablets I could only get 150 tablets, I could not get another fifty in time so I bought another hundred Russian dianabol tablets. I realize that dianabol in Canada and the United States would more then likely be fake since it has been taken off the market. The dianabol I bought was through a person who receives his stuff from Europe. I have decided to go straight to the dianabol as a type of pyramid to increase growth then cycle off on the stanozolol and dianabol. Right now I am using 20 mg of the dianabol. I have gained another five pounds, so I now weight 205 pounds. I have also noticed an impressive increase in strength. On the down side I seem to have small patches of acne on my back and chest, but it does not look like normal acne and is not noticeable except to me. I also have a tendency to become angered very quickly, but if I realize it is happening I can control it with no problem. I have also increased my calories to about 5500 a day. I am looking hard and defined and people have really started noticing. There has been little or no noticeable water retention. So far I have had no real problems with the drugs.

November 6: I now only have one shot of propionate left. I seem to be noticing a little gynecomastia. This is due to the dianabol. I now weigh 208 and my strength has gone up again. I think I will only use seventy tabs, I have jumped for this week up to five tabs a day. I feel now as I get closer to the end of my cycle that the drugs I have used were too strong.

November 13: I have taken the last injection of testosterone and have dropped to taking three tablets of dianabol. I now weigh 210, but my strength has stayed about the same. My acne has stayed the same and I think I was paranoid about loosing hair because there is no loss.

November 21: I now am taking the last of my stanozolol with the last dianabol. I am on two stanozolol and one dianabol. I am worried about losing my gains when I am off so I bought a bottle of A.P.L. this is an animal derivative of H.C.G. and also a bottle of progesterone to control the bitch tits. My strength and weight have stayed the same, no major changes.

November 28: I am taking two stanozolol tabs a day along with a two cc shot of A.P.L. and a half a cc of progesterone. I take the progesterone once every three days. My weight and strength are still the same. I have noticed another increase in my libido. This time the increase is more noticeable then before. I was able to have sex six times in one night and the erection was just as hard as the first. Also my testicles have regained their size.

December 5: I am now taking one stanozolol a day and a two and a half shot of A.P.L.. I will only take the A.P.L. for three weeks so not to destroy my own production of Luteinizing Hormone. Also taking a half cc of progesterone every three days. I now weigh 208 and my strength has yet to go down noticeably.

December 12: I am now off the stanozolol and have one shot of A.P.L. left along with a total of four shots of Progesterone. Again my strength is about the same and my weight is now at 207. Basically everything has gone well so far. In another month and a half I will give you my progress. I will now give you my peak weight and strength measurements as they were on November 13.

Weight: 210
Flat bench 245 max 300
Incline bench: 215 max 245
Squat:335 max 380
Hauk Squat: 385 max 435
Lat pull down to the chest: 260 improved my form
Seated row: 290 no max
Over head triceps extensions: 115 no max
Machine curls: 180 no max
Shoulder press: 160 no max
Upright row: 155 no max

Body Measurements

Chest 43.5	Thigh 25.25
Arms 14.5	Calf 15.5
Neck 16.5	Forearm 13

January 27: I now weigh 203 this might look like a loss but not really. My body fat is now nine and a half compared to 13.5 when on the drugs. The body fat test was done on a body analysis machine. My Basal metabolic rate is now 2413 compared to 2324 when on the drugs. I have been taking Ephedrine Hydrochloride at 100 mg a day plus 200 mg of caffeine every fourth day. This combination has worked very well for me. I also do one hour of aerobics on my days off. My strength has gone down since the cycle but now I have about 95% of my strength back and improving all the time. I do intend to use again in July. This time I will use Equipoise, 200 tabs of Anavar, Nolvadex, and Clomid. I felt it was

worth it, but I intend to use lighter drugs and have blood tests done."

"All my life I was a boney, skinny kid. Big guys would always pick on me and get me to fight them because they were twice my size. Even in my 20's I weighed 140 pounds at 5'10". Then in 1988 a friend of mine started lifting in a big gym. He got hold of some steroids, Deca-Durabolin. He got real cut and big. I could not believe it. So I bought some from him. Wow, this stuff works. I gained 40 pounds of muscle, it was great.

Then I ran out, he could not get any steroids any more. Then, all hell broke loose on steroids. I live in a small town and getting steroids is impossible. Then some people from Nova Scotia Canada said I can sell you any steroid you want. So twice I sent my money and twice I got ripped off. They took my money and I never got anything. So I went to Mexico, got testosterone and primobolan tabs. This was great it was very cheap in Mexico, but I was scared to death and I will never do that again. Then these ran out, so I started going to vets. I can get equipoise any time I want now. But they don't seem to work as good as Deca. So I stopped lifting for two years.

Now I've opened my own small gym and started lifting again. It's great, but I need steroids. What I would really like to try is Human Growth Hormone. I want to get big and stay that way, but the big problem is getting this stuff. It would be nice if the U.S. government would stay out of our personal lives. What we do to our bodies is our business. So to make a long story short, steroids worked for me with no problems. I got big and felt good about myself. I want to be that way again. P.S. The amount of steroids I took are low compared to most bodybuilders and they still worked good."

A couple of years ago there was a guy operating out of Canada who would advertise a book, "Steroid Report", in several bodybuilding publications. He never wrote the book. When people ordered the book he would send them back a steroid price list and order form. The order form set a minimum order and it requested that cash or money orders made out to cash be sent to a Canadian post office box. People that placed orders never received anything. Eventually, the readers of the various publications that he advertised in complained to the publications and the publications stopped running the ads. This guy's scam is partially responsible for Muscle and Fitness and Flex no longer accepting ads that mention steroids.

After being blackballed by the magazines the guy started purchasing mailing lists from companies involved with bodybuilding. Then he continued his scam by sending his price list and order form to the people on the mailing lists. The United States and Canadian Postal services tried to tack the guy down for several years. They had trouble finding him because he never stayed in one place for very long. He would send out a wave of price lists, collect his orders, move on to a new town, and then do it all over again. Every time he moved he changed his name and the name of the business. Another problem with catching him was that people who had been ripped off trying to order illegal drugs though the mail were reluctant to notify the authorities. Finally, after three or four years of running this scam the guy was caught and put in prison. Nobody knows how many hundreds of thousands of dollars he made.

"A friend of mine was very against the use of steroids. About 5 years ago, he was around 20 and he had been training for 4 years without steroids. One day at the gym someone came with what was called clenbuterol. He said it was a great product but it was not a steroid nor was it dangerous at all. My friend gave it a try and was very pleased with the results. He discovered it was easier to get big and to stay lean. Today, he is very much into steroid use as clenbuterol totally changed his mind."

As your friend experienced first hand, both clenbuterol and steroids have significant anabolic effects. However, it is important to remember that both of these products can cause negative side effects. Clenbuterol may be safer than steroids, but this does not mean that it is not dangerous at all. In addition, clenbuterol is not as effective an anabolic agent as steroids are.

"Like many other natural bodybuilders out there, I fell victim to all the "Hype" that has surrounded clenbuterol over the last couple of years. All the articles that proclaimed this stuff to be some kind of wonder drug that could one day make steroids obsolete were difficult to ignore. While on a trip to Europe, I managed to purchase some "Spiropent"-clenbuterol over the counter in Germany (a 3 months supply) which cast about $2 Canadian per box of 20. This was the only size they came in. Upon my return to Canada, I couldn't wait to get started training. I took 4 tablets, spaced out over the course of the day for 2 days then took none for the next 2 days. I repeated this 2 on 2 off cycle for 3 months.

In all honesty, I must admit that my training did seem to get a kick in it initially. I felt like I had more energy and noticed a little added strength. Nothing to write home about, though. At first I thought "All right" this clenbuterol is legitimate, but after about a week I noticed absolutely no positive effect on my workouts. I continued on until my 3 month supply was used up, hoping, I guess that the wonder drug would kick-in and transform me into a Mr. Olympia.

Looking back now I attribute the initial gain in energy and strength to my 1 week lay off while in Europe. We all know how a break form the weights every once in a while can be beneficial to our progress. Also, since I was so geared up expecting the clenbuterol to do miracles for me I believe a placebo effect was at play as well. Granted, this is no scientific study, but merely one man's experience. I just feel that all the hype about clenbuterol is just that, hype. And what really burns me is that there's people out there selling it for as much as $100 for 100 tabs! I certainly didn't pay that much and feel like I was ripped of big time. I can only imagine how pissed off some of you are that paid big bucks for this junk!

Just to wrap up, I don't condone steroid use. I've used steroids myself and decided that I prefer to remain natural. I don't believe it's worth it long-term for short term gains. But I will be the first to say that steroid do work, there's no doubt about it which is a lot more than can be said for all those supplements flooding the market. Makes you wonder how Joe Weider, the self professed fitness guru of the 20th century, can in good conscience put all those bogus ads in his magazines-But then that's another story."

There are many possible reasons for your experience with clenbuterol turning out as it did. You may have purchased a counterfeit product or you may have been taking weak doses of a legit product. However, it seems more likely to me that you, as you mentioned in your letter, had extremely high expectations for clenbuterol due to all of the articles that have been written about clenbuterol. While it is true that clenbuterol has anabolic effects it is misleading to claim that clenbuterol is as powerful as anabolic steroids. Clenbuterol gained popularity among athletes because it is harder to detect and safer than anabolic steroids. I do not think that anyone who has used steroids and clenbuterol would say that they are equally effective. It is likely that clenbuterol and other b2-agonists will be used more frequently by athletes in the future. This increased use will be due more to the inability of drug testing procedures to detect new anabolic agents than these agents actually being more powerful than anabolic steroids.

"A friend of mine from college was working out on a daily basis and really going nowhere. He scored some D-Ball and some testosterone cypionate and really started showing progress. He went from 175 pounds to 205 pounds in three months. That was the good part of the cycle. The bad part was that boils developed all over his back, chest, and face. He also got really aggressive when he drank alcohol. His hair thinned out a bit and he claims that his sex drive dropped for quite a while after the cycle. He still has some gynecomastia. He ate everything in sight and drank tons of milk. He looked like he was pumped full of air. He no longer cycles because he says that nothing out there is real any longer. He still trains but is back down to about 185 pounds. Still aggressive when he drinks also."

It is quite possible that your friend's sex drive dropped for a time after the cycle. Anabolic steroids make the testes atrophy. The testes shrink in size and decrease or completely stop testosterone production. Testosterone is responsible for the male sex drive. During a cycle anabolic steroids take the place of the testosterone that the testes usually produce. This keeps the sex drive healthy. In fact, because athletes often take several times the amount of anabolic steroids that the testes are capable of producing, the sex drive often increases during a cycle. However, at the end of a cycle the testes remain atrophied and anabolic steroids are no longer being taken. In the absence of normal testosterone production by the testes and exogenous anabolic steroids sex drive is likely to decrease. Fortunately, the testes almost always resume normal testosterone production within a few months. The loss of sex drive can be diminished by gradually tapering doses down towards the end of the cycle.

"A friend of mine was really under weight and had a bad self esteem. He was being picked on quite a bit. So he tried all the weight gain drinks and different training programs. Nothing happened at all. He found a doctor who prescribed him anabolic steroids.
<u>Bottom Line</u>
They helped him gain the weight he needed which improved his self esteem which made his life much more enjoyable. By the way the guy who used to pick on him... I'm sure he still thinks about my friend when he removes his dentures. I know violence isn't cool, but this guy would just not let up on my friend. In other words, he deserved it."

We have all been in situations where we would like to assume the physique of Arnold and kick someone's face in. The famous sand kicked in the face on the beach/lost girl friend ad tapped into this desire and helped to sell hundreds of thousands of books on weight training. However, when steroids come into the picture there are some important facts that need to be remembered. Teenagers should never take anabolic steroids. Anabolic steroids can stop bone growth. Teenagers that take anabolic steroids in order to get big often end up making themselves smaller for the rest of their lives. They never reach their bodies full growth potential due to the premature stoppage of bone grow that anabolic steroids cause. The question is simple: Would you rather be bigger than the other guy for a few years or for the rest of your life?

"I renewed my interest in bodybuilding after many years. I bought a gym membership at Gold's Gym Venice in 1988 and started working out. Over a period of years I bought every supplement advertised in the popular magazines including: Frac, Boron, Dibencozide, Chromium Picolinate, Hot Stuff, Metabolol 2, Pro Optibol, Adrenal Gland Concentrate, Ultimate Orange, Cytomax, Grow 2000, Amino Acids, and on and on. The amount of money I spent on this junk was the only thing that was getting massive. I figured that some supplement would help make me bigger and better but that was not the case. Hard work and consistency pays off better for the truly natural bodybuilder.

Later I figured I wanted to be outstanding and would try to find some steroids. I had no idea how or where to start. I got ripped off by some mail order steroid ad and figured it would be too much effort to try to find someone who would sell me the real deal. My priorities are changing so much that maybe being massive isn't as important anymore. I love bodybuilding, but I know that all you need is the right connections to get big."

"I have been bodybuilding/weight lifting for about 10 years. Within this time my knowledge of the sport along with my knowledge of steroids also grew. I enjoyed moderate success and weight gains trying a variety of supplements and claims made by different companies. It wasn't until two years ago though that I had the opportunity to try a cycle of Winstrol.

Let me tell you the difference was almost immediate. My physique took on a more finished look and more solidness and fullness. I also found that I recuperated a lot faster and was always up and ready for my next workout. That summer, the summer of 90, I looked the best I ever did!!! All my friends, relatives, and coworkers all noticed. Since then however my use of steroids has been far and in between due to the fact that my source has not been able to obtain them because of tighter restrictions.

In short, however, my experience was most definitely a positive one, and I will continue to use them whenever possible."

"I was hoping you could help me deal with these steroids I've been taking for medical reasons. I've been taking steroids via a nasal spray-they are called Nasacort and Vancenase.

The problems I've been having is I've been getting gynecomastia, cushing goid features which is basically obesity especially in my face, my bones have been getting bigger, from head to foot, especially in my jaw and chin, and I've been getting really hairy.

I wouldn't mind all of my bones to continue growing if it weren't making my chin and jaw bigger. It seems that my chin and jaw are growing bigger than the rest of my bones so that they are growing out of proportion. I think I'd continue taking these steroids if there were some way of stopping the growth of my chin and jaw so that the rest of my body could maybe catch up with the size of my head.

I do mind all this hair growth because I was extremely hairy to begin with and now I'm starting to get hair on my back."

It is difficult to give you precise answers to your questions without knowing what medical reasons you are taking steroids for and the dosages and frequency of your steroid use. Hopefully, you have discussed these problems with your doctor and he has given you some options. If your medical conditions permit the best solution may be to discontinue steroid use completely. If this is not an option there are certain steroids and means of administering these steroids that may alleviate some of your problems.

Anabolic steroid receptor sites can be found in tissues throughout the body. There are anabolic steroid receptor sites in your chin, jaw, skeletal muscle, and many other areas. It is possible that nasal spray administration of steroids is delivering higher doses of steroids to your chin and jaw than to other areas your body because your chin and jaw are close to your nose. If you were to inject steroids directly into the muscle, or other portion of your body that you are trying to improve by using steroids, this area would receive more steroids than your chin and jaw. As a result, you would experience more growth in the targeted area and less growth in your chin and jaw. Once all of the anabolic steroid receptor sites in the targeted area are full continued steroid use can easily raise steroid blood levels high enough to promote excess growth in the chin, jaw, and other unintended areas.

Decreasing the dosages and frequency of steroid use will decrease the side effects that you are experiencing. In addition, some steroids have weaker masculinizing effects (e.g. promoting hair growth) and stronger anabolic, tissue building, effects than others. Anavar is one such steroid. Female bodybuilders prefer steroids like anavar because of their weaker masculinizing effects. However, even these steroids, if taken in high enough dosages can promote extreme masculinization.

The most common cause of gynecomastia is the peripheral conversion of anabolic steroids to estrogen. Estrogen promotes female characteristics like breast development. Some anabolic steroids, such as mesterolone, fluoxymesterolone, and dihydrotestosterone can not be converted to estrogen. These steroids are far less likely to cause gynecomastia than other steroids that can be converted to estrogen.

"I started training 6 years ago. I moved to a new location and there was a gym nearby. It was geared to the fitness crowd and there were no hard-core bodybuilders. I read Muscle and Fitness faithfully and followed Weider's wisdom. It soon became apparent the guys (and girls) featured in the magazines were using more than Weider's mega-anabolic packs, I couldn't find any info on the subject but I did find a doctor who would prescribe me steroids-Deca.

I knew nothing about steroids and unfortunately the doctor knew even less. He told me to take 1 or 2 vials a week and that to stay big I would have to stay on them like the pros. After 4 months I knew I wasn't making any further gains. the doctor then gave me anadrol and said to take 2 or 3 a day. I made more gains and picked up every known side effect along the way. After 2 months on anadrol I wanted off drugs. The doctor put men on H.C.G.. I started to lose size rapidly and felt the pits. The doctor switched to Clomid and then I kept the size left and felt a whole lot better. I stayed off drugs for 5 months and upon resuming, I did only 1/2 a vial a week but stayed on for 8 months because I didn't want to go through withdrawal again. When I finally came off I used clomid for 6 weeks then a product called ORCHIC Testosterone Extract by Gray Market. It helped me keep my gains and I felt great. Unfortunately the product was hard to get and when my supply ran out I lost some size but was still in very good shape.

I now thought I knew what I was doing. I stayed off all supplements for 5 months. When I resumed using Deca I got gains for the first couple of weeks and then the drug stopped working and I lost size and strength. I was then put on Test. cyp. and then Primo-bolan with the same results. they would work for a week or 2 then nothing and sometimes I would go backwards and lose gains. The doctor figured my system had become saturated with the drugs and that I should find other products to use. Around this time Clenbuterol was hitting the scene. I used Spiropent and for 2 weeks I got unbelievably huge and cut then boom in 2 or 3 days I would lose it all. The same thing happened with Dymetadrine 25 and even when not using these products for 6 months, when resuming use they might work a few days then nothing. I have used Methacil, DCP, GABA, Vanadyl Sulfate, Cyclofenil, all with the same results. I used Cyasteroine and in 2 weeks I gained a solid 10 pounds and became very lean anadrol worked for 3 weeks and then the gains slid away in a few days even while still taking the product at a larger dose.

I can feel when the products switch from working phenomenally well to not working at all and in a few days I will be back to where I started. This is very frustrating. I stayed off Cyasterone 5 months and when using it again I got hardly anything from it. It was at the time I started using these steroid alternatives that I started getting MuscleMag International. I read some of their steroid articles and discovered that everything I had been doing was dead wrong. Using too much, too long, not switching to other drugs besides Deca. I was wondering if you have come across my problem and can give me details on what can be done. I am truly hoping I haven't screwed myself up royally. The few times I used what would be considered moderate dosages of Deca, I got fantastic gains. If I had the knowledge before hand I feel that I could have gotten great gains on small amounts for short cycles.

With the alternatives out there now that worked I may not have had to use steroids to get the physique I want. Now nothing works. I feel I could have built an impressive physique with the drugs used if I had the knowledge beforehand. Any info on what I can do to remedy this problem would be most gratefully appreciated. The censorship of providing facts and most of the major magazines denial of steroids in any form is a complete crock. I only hope more people have access to your work, so that if they decide to use drugs, they can use them and avoid the problems I have incurred. I would think that the pros and the large amounts they use and the long time they are on drugs there must be ways of solving my problem. I would like to turn things around and start making gains in a knowledgeable manner. Thank you for taking the time to read this letter, and I hope I have provided enough information for you to give me a reply."

When you were taking high doses of steroids for long periods of time you built the cortisol level in your blood up to an extremely high point. You reached plateaus because after a while the cortisol level was comparable to the large amounts of steroids that you were taking. When you got off of the steroids you crashed and lost most of your gains because the cortisol was now able to exert its effect through receptor sites that had once been occupied by anabolic steroid molecules.

Shorter 6 to 8 week cycles are safer and more effective than the 8 month cycle that you described. The cortisol imbalance created by an 8 month cycle can last for several months. It might take longer than 5 months for the cortisol level to return to normal and for you to start getting the kinds of results you initially got. The pyramid method can be use to combat this problem. In essence, the pyramid method recognizes that a plateau will be reached. It delays plateauing by gradually working up to a maximum level of steroid consumption. The plateau is reached at the peak of the cycle. Phasing out steroid use slowly by gradually tapering dosages down maintains the plateau by maintaining a situation where the ratio of anabolic to catabolic hormones is equal. This allow one to hold on to gains for a longer period of time. No drug, not even anabolic steroids, can provide unlimited, continuous growth. Thus, a number of short cycles, using the pyramid method, with a drug free period in between must be utilized to get the maximum effect of anabolic steroids.

"I am delighted to know that you have given people that have used anabolic steroids a chance to share what steroids have done for them. How it has improved their workouts or how its been a disadvantage. As for me, it has been a very good help not too long ago.

I was on a six week cycle of Equipoise. Needless to say I was on it very heavy about 2-4 cc's every other day then it was 4 cc's M-F however I didn't experience any real bad side effects none at all. I couldn't believe how humongous I had grown.

About the fourth week I began to feel very uncomfortable because I was tight all over. I felt like I was in a body suit all day long after my cycle of course this little side effects wore off. I still kept my size because I was constantly working out. I became totally in love with myself. I felt I was better looking than everyone. I would get upset when the women would touch me. I just didn't want anyone touching me it was hands off or else. I noticed that I was always in the mirror. It got so bad that I had to go and see a psychiatrist. I lost my girlfriend because of my change of character.

I am glad that I am off. I can't say I won't take them anymore because in the near future I do plan on working on growing but in the mean time I have been doing it of course naturally. I just want to leave this with anyone who plans on using anabolic steroids. The decision is yours you make it not anyone else."

"Through out my life I had always been overweight. When I was 25 I started taking one injection of winstrol v a week. I immediately started to lose body fat and gain muscle quick. A few months went by and in that short period of time I had lost forty pounds of fat and gained twenty pounds of muscle. I was actually seeing my dreams come true. I decided I wanted to compete. I set a date on my calendar and started training. Knowing I would need to put on extra muscle mass I started taking one anadrol-50 per week.

Well to make a long story short I won the overall at that show and many more since. My doctor says I am as healthy as could be. I am a living example that you can take steroids and live a happy healthy life."

"As many others, I too was in a slump. I had spent hundreds of dollars on over the counter supplements and costly work out schedules that never gave me the gains that I was looking for. So when offered the other alternative-steroids-I decided to give it a try. I had never seen, purchased ore used steroids before. I purchased what I was told was an "8 week cycle of killer stuff."

After failed attempts to draw the liquid through the needle because it was so thick, I pulled the needle out and poured the liquid in. When I did I spilled some on my fingers. Out of curiosity I licked my fingers. Boy what a surprise to find this steroid tasted like cooking oil a lot like cooking oil. The next day at the gym I over heard a guy saying he was burned on a deal by receiving a vial of cooking oil for what he thought was steroids from the same guy I just bought from. Boy was I out some $!"

Cooking oil is frequently used by scam artists as a counterfeit steroid. Cooking oil resembles some steroids because many steroids are oil based. Specific oils, that can be drawn through the needle, have been found to help the body absorb steroids. As you learned, if you expect that some one is trying to sell you cooking oil, you can taste and or try to draw the suspected counterfeit through a needle. It should be noted that some legitimate steroids can not be drawn through small needles.

Unfortunately, the counterfeit steroid industry is getting more sophisticated all the time. People that were familiar with the packaging that steroids come in used to be able to detect counterfeits by comparison. However, counterfeiters have gotten so good at duplicating the packaging that many counterfeits are almost undetectable.

After a great deal of tedious comparison some discrepancies that tip off the counterfeit may be found. For example, if the I.D. code and expiration date are printed on in the same black ink as the rest of the box and label it is likely that the product in question is a counterfeit. Most manufactures print I.D. codes and expiration dates in color so the important information that they convey stands out.

Counterfeit Primobolan 50 mg tablets are currently popular. The counterfeiting job is well done. The scored tablets are duplicated so well that they pass visual inspection and the unique glass bottle and plastic stopper are extremely close to the ones used by Schering. The I.D. code and expiration date are the only things that would raise suspicion among the experienced consumer as they are printed in the same black ink as the rest of the packaging.

Some times the only way to determine whether a product is counterfeit is to have it analyzed by a testing facility. Unfortunately, this is not practical for the average consumer due to the laws and the fact that it costs about $1000 to have one product tested. The only way to control the counterfeit problem is to legalize steroids. Until legalization is a reality, which will most likely be a long long time if ever, counterfeiters will continue to have a substantial advantage.

"My friend Bob was 28 years old he was determined to make bodybuilding progress. He was 6'4" tall and was tired of being thin. He tried many methods of gaining weight and building muscle and these methods had only been minimally successful. He decided to try steroids namely, methandrostenalone and later stacked this with deca-durabolin.

To make a long story short, in about five months his weight went from 195 pounds to 245 pounds. About this time he began to develop strange feelings in his chest and went to the doctor who indicated that the problem was a heart arrhythmia.

The doctor also indicated that Bob's cholesterol was high (over 300) and his HDL level was very low, thus making him a prime candidate for a heart attack.

Of course, Bob was very alarmed and discontinued steroid use. Two months latter his cholesterol was 190 and his HDL level was acceptable. Bob did not keep the mass he had gained and his weight plummeted to 189 pounds.

Today, 10 years later, Bob is still lifting and trying to make progress, but has not been able to get past 215 pounds. At the time of Bob's steroid use, he was following a very high fat, high sodium diet and this certainly may have contributed to his problems."

Anabolic steroids are known to significantly alter lipoprotein (cholesterol) levels. Lipoprotein levels may reach a dangerous point. An individual that has a family history of heart attacks may suffer from a heart attack earlier, due to anabolic steroid use, than he would have purely as a result of his genealogy. Cholesterol levels usually return to normal approximately one month after steroid use has been discontinued.

"I had a friend who used steroids because he got whatever he wanted free. Totes and tote bags of steroids would be in his house. Anadrol-50, testosterone propionate, decanoate, deca-durabolin, bumex, nolvadex, needles. He started taking everything he got his hands on. He started with 1 or 2 anadrol daily till he got to 6-9 cc's and 10 anadrols every day 9 cc's in his ass and 10 anadrols in a Hot Stuff shake.

He was crazy, incredible strength and he was a diabetic. He was ripped and was hard as a rock without flexing. He went from benching 140 pounds to 250 pounds in about 2 or 3 weeks.

He was dealing, using, giving away for free he had so much. Selling anadrol for $30-$50 a bottle depending if it was a friend or not. His mind was not his anymore. His mind was owned by the steroids, until he started beating people with his juice buddies on the weekend. He was a madman until he sold to the wrong person and got busted. Now he is still waiting for trial with $100,000 bail which can't be posted. He is in deep shit now. He is probably getting weaker, smaller, and sicker and all his friends as well."

Anabolic steroid use is extremely dangerous for diabetics. Diabetics take insulin to treat their condition. Insulin can cause dangerous chemical interactions when taken with steroids. Insulin and steroids should never be used at the same time.

"A good friend of mine is in his late 60's. He was an outstanding high school and college athlete who had to turn down some promising offers for semi pro and professional sports due to severe family problems and obligations.

He had excelled in football, track and field, and boxing. He managed to stay with boxing and an occasional marathon. He was an exciting club fighter and kept an impressive unbeaten record. He turned down many offers to pursue a boxing career not wanting to take anything away from his family. He set his dreams for later years and being able to compete in the Senior Olympics.

He maintained an adequate gym in his garage with speed bags, body bag, weights, and a stair master, but he could not bring his body to function as he needed and wanted. One of his friends introduced him to growth hormone and its research and a macro biotic diet. He has been using growth hormone for almost one year and his training has improved to two hours of gym work in the am and 1 and 1/2 hours pm and he easily jogs five miles every day. He looks like he could compete in a bodybuilding show and he is definitely a fierce competitor, looking for his shot at the Senior Olympics. He looks and acts like a person twenty years younger. His youthful zest has returned and I have never seen him so happy, healthy, and full of life."

Human growth hormone, some times in conjunction with anabolic steroids, has been promoted by many as a fountain of youth. Several companies, most of them located south of the border, advertise their human growth hormone clinics in Longevity Magazine. These clinics offer medically supervised administration of growth hormone. They claim that their growth hormone therapy is life extending. While there is evidence, as the preceding letter illustrates, that growth hormone can make the body look younger there is no conclusive evidence that growth hormone is a life extender. In addition, if growth hormone is misused severe side effects that can lead to early death may occur.

"I had a friend that weighed about 170 pounds and was about 5'6" tall. He wasn't fat just a little over weight. He found out about winstrol-v and bought some from a friend of his. (10 CC-for $90) He took a CC every other day for 20 days and worked out hard (weight lifting, jogging, and aerobics) At the end of the cycle he weighed 135 pounds and was as solid as a rock. Everyone was excited with his results and started buying steroids to get ripped-up like he did. By the way, I know of no one that has had any side effects yet so everything is all right. I was thinking about getting on the roids."

Anabolic Steroids cause bone growth to stop prematurely. Your friends, if they began using steroids before they stopped growing, are likely to be shorter than they would have been had they not used steroids.

"About 4 months ago I met a friend who was able to get any type of steroids. Boy, was he living proof that steroids do work wonders. I was very anxious to try some for myself so I bought a 2 month supply of dianabol and methyltestosterone.

I had them analyzed by my chemistry teacher to see if they really were steroids. He took them to his lab and the next day he told me they were pure steroids and he mentioned the fact that they were very powerful drugs.

I took 4 pills a day (20 mg) just like my friend did and I worked out like a madman 5 days a week. The weeks went by and nothing happened. I still only weighed 170 pounds at a height of 6 feet 1 inch. I was so pissed but I still kept with the month program. At the end of my cycle I still weighed only 170 pounds. All my dreams of being huge were shattered. To this day, I still can't get over that experience with steroids.

Do steroids work for everyone? If they don't work for everyone, then what is the reason why?"

There are many possible reasons for your steroid experience turning out as it did. However, there is only one probable reason for your lack of results.

There are some rare diseases that inhibit the bodies ability to bind to and process anabolic steroid molecules. Hypercortisolemia (high cortisol levels) and hypogonadism (malfunctioning, damaged, or non existent testes) can also decrease the effectiveness of anabolic steroids. However, if you had such a condition it would most likely have exhibited itself in the form of a lack of energy and muscle. 6"1', 170 pounds is quite scrawny, but it is not at all uncommon. Furthermore, you were physically able to work out like a "madman" even though you did not get the results that you had hoped for.

If you were not eating sufficiently large amounts of food while taking steroids you would not have experienced the weight and muscle gain that you expected. You knew that you had to exercise to get results

80

so I am sure that you knew that you had to eat properly too.

So you see there are many possible reasons for your experience, but in the final analysis there is only one reason that is likely. That reason, as you have probably guessed, is that you were not taking what you though you were taking. Both of the steroids that you have mentioned have been widely counterfeited. In some cases these counterfeits contain no steroid material at all, while in other cases the counterfeits contain small amounts of anabolic steroids. Your chemistry teacher may have detected these small amounts and assumed the product was legit or your chemistry teacher may have switched pills on you as teachers are trained to oppose drug use.

If you still believe that what you were taking was legit you may want to see a doctor because there are a few rare diseases that could be responsible for your experience.

"I and my friend recently made a trip to Mexico. While there we thought we'd see if it was possible to buy steroids over the counter.

Evidently Mexico has new laws where to buy steroids one must have a prescription. We quickly found out prescriptions were no problem. Basically "fake" doctors' offices were set up and had recruiters to get patients off the streets. For a very small fee it was possible to get a prescription for whatever you pleased. This prescription is not legal in the U.S..

Anyway the trip was great and we learned a lot from the people there. Looking forward to visiting again soon."

Some Mexican pharmacies that are located near the U.S. border and have a large number of U.S. customers have started asking for prescriptions. As you experienced, a little extra money can usually get you what you want in Mexico. Most of the pharmacies located farther from the U.S. border do not require prescriptions for anabolic steroids and do not sell counterfeit steroids. Most of the testosterone cypionate and Winstrol-V that is sold in Tijuana and other Mexican border towns is counterfeit. The counterfeits are made in America and sold to Mexican pharmacies by counterfeit dealers. One tip off to these counterfeits is that they are usually cheaper than the real steroids that are sold in Mexico.

Sostenon 250, Primobolan 5mg tablets, pre-load Deca Durabolin syringes, Spiropent (clenbuterol), Fertodur (cyclofenil), and HCG from Mexico are usually authentic. However, if you get caught at the border with these items, real or counterfeit, you will be in deep shit.

"I have always been a very thin person until recently when I had my first experience with steroids. In high school I was 6'3" at 140 lbs. I looked like I had just come off the boat from Ethiopia. I ate like a horse but never gained an ounce. Doctors always told me that I was in perfect health and that my thin condition was normal. Classmates teased me all through my high school years. With this abuse I developed a complex about the way I looked. I am now 24 years old still 6'3" and now weight 215lbs. That is a 75 pound increase over a six year period. Part of this weight increase is due to my experience with steroids.

I was able to obtain 100% pure pharmaceutical grade steroids from a close friend that is closely associated with the medical field and deals with several nationally known drug suppliers. So I felt safe about the ingredients and potency of the drugs. I took a total of two cycles each consisting of an eight week period. Over this eight week period I took eight injections of testosterone cypionate and nandrolone decanoate. The testosterone cypionate came in a 10 ml sterile multiple dose vial (200 mg/ml) and the nandrolone decanoate came in a 2 ml multiple dose vial (100 mg/ml). A cycle consisted of the following displayed over an eight week period with the injections measured in cc's:

Week	T.C.	N.D.
1	1cc	1cc
2	1.5cc	1cc
3	1.5cc	2cc
4	2cc	2cc
5	1.5cc	2cc
6	1.5cc	1cc
7	.5cc	.5cc
8	.5cc	.5cc

I was told that this cycle was rather safe in terms of the average cycles that have been used by bodybuilders in the past.

I started a six day split training routine in July of 1993 and this is when I took my first cycle. during this cycle I noticed an immediate increase in energy. I had trouble sleeping and had symptoms of nausea. My workouts were much more intense and rewarding. I felt confident since I had some help from the steroids. By the end of the cycle my size had increased significantly along with my strength. However, by the end of the cycle I looked a little bloated especially in the face. I think that the benefits from the steroids could have been more rewarding had I been working out prior to my first cycle. At the present time my overall workout has much improved since July. After I went off my first cycle I noticed a steady decline in my size which stopped after a certain point but I did not return to my original size. I felt weaker and was mentally tormented by the fact that I was dwindling away. However, I continued with my workout as usual and did my second cycle in December of 1993. The positive effects were much more noticeable and the negative effects were much less noticeable on this second cycle. When I was finished with my second cycle I again had increased in size significantly and I seem to have retained more of my size than what I retained with the first cycle. The second cycle hasn't affected me as much psychologically as the first cycle because I wasn't expecting a miracle and I had already experienced a cycle and new what to expect. I was recently informed that the manufacturer has discontinued the steroids I was using so I suppose any more experience with steroids is not in the cards for me unless I find another manufacturer that still makes them. For now I will just have to continue working out with not influence from steroids.

Now my question is: How intense was the cycle I took in comparison to what has been done by other steroid users? How much progress should I expect from a cycle of the caliber I experienced? What are the major risks associated with a cycle of this caliber and how will this affect my overall health and longevity?"

The cycle that you took would be considered an average pre-contest cycle by most competitive bodybuilders. Of course, competitive bodybuilders often take several other drugs at the same time and there will always be some nut cases that decide to consume absurd amounts of steroids. From a cycle of the caliber that you experienced you should expect to gain 15-20 pounds and notice a definite increase in strength. The majority of the weight gain should be in the form of muscle (provided that you are working out and eating sufficiently), but a portion of it will be due to increased water retention and fat.

The major risks associated with a cycle of this caliber are minimal. It is theoretically possible that you could experience some of the major side effects mentioned in this book from such a cycle, but this is highly unlikely. In addition to the common minor side effects that you described you may also experience testicular atrophy and acne. It is likely that there would be some effects on your overall health and longevity if you were to take such a cycle over and over for many years. As you experienced, most of the gains made while on steroids are lost once steroid use is discontinued. Steroid use is not really a solution for your problem unless you want to use steroids for the rest of your life which would be both expensive and dangerous.

6

ALTERNATIVES TO ANABOLIC STEROID USE

Products that promote muscle growth and or athletic performance are big business. It is impossible to flip through a bodybuilding magazine without being bombarded by ads for products that claim to increase muscle size and strength. Many of these products are touted as replacements for anabolic steroids. Ads try to convince the reader that the advertised product will work just as well, or better than anabolic steroids without causing any negative side effects. The fact is that the vast majority of these products are worthless. Any product that truly is as powerful as anabolic steroids would, most likely, be illegal as it would have negative side effects. Medicines and supplements have to adhere to specific guidelines in order to be sold without a prescription. These guidelines are more concerned with making sure that the product will not hurt the consumer than actually making sure that the product is effective. Once these guidelines are met the product, if it were ever truly effective in the first place, is usually reduced to an extremely weak or totally ineffective level. The success of such products can be credited to effective advertising and the placebo effect. Furthermore, the vast sums of money involved with such products have bred wide spread fraud. People are eager to cash in on the sale of products designed to increase performance beyond what would normally be achieved without them, ergogenic products. Most of these people do not care if they rip off or harm the consumer in the process.

There are no miracle products that can replace anabolic steroids by providing the benefits of steroids without the side effects. However, effective alternatives to anabolic steroids do exist. These alternatives include everything from going natural to the use of potent drugs like human growth hormone.

Staying natural has advantages that appeal to many people. Obviously, there are no side effects involved with staying natural and there is no need to get involved in illegal activities. Furthermore, the natural athlete does not fall victim to the belief that his improvement and or success is due solely to the use of certain drugs. This helps the natural athlete maintain a vital characteristic that is essential to all champions, self confidence. Many athletes that use drugs lose there self confidence when they are not on drugs. As a result, they are forced to abuse drugs in order to maintain their self confidence. Athletics is a mind game. To be successful, you must believe in yourself. You must have supreme confidence. Some of the most physically gifted and coordinated athletes in the world are never successful because they choke under pressure. They lose faith in themselves and they let their brains kill their chances of doing what their bodies can do. Supreme confidence is more crucial to success than any ergogenic aid. Supreme confidence allows athletes to succeed in the worlds of sport and business.

Most highly effective ergogenic drugs, like anabolic steroids, are, in the United States, only available through the black-market or by prescription. Human growth hormone is one of these drugs. HGH has become popular due to its growth inducing properties and the fact that it can not be detected through current urine based drug tests. There are two FDA approved brands of synthetic HGH, Protropin produced by Genetech, San Francisco, and Humatrope produced by Eli Lilly, Indianapolis. Foreign, natural HGH is also available. The brands are Crescormon, Pharmacia Labs, and Assellacrin, Serano Labs. They are made from the pituitary glands of cadavers and can contain a number of active viruses.[68] Use in the United States was banned after four patients developed Creutzfeldt-Jacob disease, a deadly virus that literally eats your brain.[69] The process for producing HGH was recently improved. The gene for HGH is inserted into a special strain of escherichia coli bacteria. This makes the bacteria produce HGH. This process has increased the availability of HGH. However, HGH is still quite expensive. Legal treatment involving HGH can run from $5,000-$30,000 per annual dosage. On the black-market prices are raised several fold.

The only approved use for HGH is treatment of children that fail to grow due to lack of adequate endogenous growth hormone secretion. Short children that have been given synthetic HGH have been found to out grow control groups by six to nine inches within four years.[70] They increase the number and size of their muscle cells and a general reduction of body fat often occurs.[71] The recommended dosage for Protropin, up to 0.1 mg (0.2 IU) per kg body weight three times per week, should not be exceeded due to the risk of potential side effects.[72]

The abuse potential of HGH is great. Many parents are tempted to give HGH to their children in order to allow them to grow taller than they would naturally grow. The temptation to do this is especially high if the child is involved with sports such as basketball. In addition, parents own dissatisfaction with being short may encourage them to take actions to make sure that their children will be tall. HGH works on children that have no growth hormone deficiency.[73] If adolescents are given doses higher than those recommended by the manufacturer they grow even faster.[74] HGH also works on adults, but it does not make them taller. The only study of HGH on athletes showed a 4% increase in lean mass and a 12% reduction in body fat.[75]

Several organs participate in the processing of HGH. These organs, the liver, thyroid, pancreas, and kidneys, must be healthy if HGH is to work well. In addition, over 8,000 calories a day, far beyond the average bodies capacity to digest food and get rid of waste, are needed to adequately fuel the growth that HGH can induce. Many bodybuilders that have weakened their livers from anabolic steroid use can not handle the extra burden that HGH puts on their livers.

Anecdotal reports suggest that HGH may allow healthy individuals to put on 30-40 pounds of lean mass in as little as three months.[76] However, the muscle created from HGH is not as strong as it should be and serious side effects can occur. It is hypothesized that HGH greatly increases production of muscle connective tissue while causing a minimal increase in contractile elements that make muscle strong. This means that an individual that built muscles through the use of HGH is likely to get tired easily and to be weak in proportion to his muscle size. Increased production of muscle connective tissue implies that HGH is likely to strengthen tendons and ligaments. As a result, some athletes that have built their bodies with the help of anabolic steroids, which are poor at building connective tissue, use HGH to strengthen their connective tissue. It is thought that this practice will prevent injury to tendons and ligaments which is common among anabolic steroid users. As mentioned previously, such polypharmacy can be dangerous as both anabolic steroids and HGH have significant side effects.

Acromegaly is one of the worst side effects of HGH. In adult individuals HGH will not promote linear bone growth, but it will cause bones to grow thicker. Internal organs, including the heart and kidneys, also increase in size. Signs of acromegaly are especially prominent in facial bones and the bones of the hands and feet. A bigger jaw, fatter nose, and a thickened shelf of ape-man bone above the eyes are common features of acromegaly.[77] Extreme hair growth and coarsening of the skin are other prominent signs of acromegaly. Acromegaly is a serious problem that leads to early death in almost all individuals that are afflicted with it. People with excess levels of HGH in their blood rarely live past 60.[78] Other problems with HGH use include: antibody formation, hepatitis, hypoglycemia, diabetes, and carpal tunnel syndrome, intense wrist nerve pain that, in many cases, may only be relieved through a surgical procedure[79]

Insulin is one of the key substances responsible for muscle growth in the human body. However, insulin works in conjunction with a number of chemical reactions in order to produce muscle growth. Insulin injections alone will not cause muscle growth because the artificially elevated insulin level requires an artificially elevated human growth hormone level to produces muscle growth promoting insulin like growth factor 1. For this reason, some athletes use insulin in conjunction with human growth hormone. This is an extremely dangerous practice. As stated above, there are several serious side effects that can stem from the use of human growth hormone. Insulin use can also cause serious problems. Safe dosages of insulin vary from person to person and can be influenced by brand, diet, use of alcohol, and use of other drugs. In fact, insulin may interact dangerously with anabolic steroids, specifically Methyltestosterone. It is easy to overdose on insulin. Too much insulin causes hypoglycemia. The brain does not get enough glucose and diabetic coma, seizures, and sudden death can occur.

Human chorionic gonadotropin is used to increases the production of endogenous testosterone. Higher levels of endogenous testosterone increases the bodies muscle building capabilities. HCG is also used to prevent testicular atrophy. HCG may cause changes in fat distribution including gynecomastia.[80] Gonadotropin Releasing Hormone and Luteinizing hormone releasing hormone (gonadorelin hydrochloride, FACTREL) can also be used to increase the production of endogenous testosterone.

Erythropoietin is a natural hormone produced by the kidneys that increases the body's oxygen carrying capacity by stimulating bone marrow to increase production of red blood cells. Increasing the body's oxygen carrying capacity leads to an increase in aerobic endurance. Erythropoietin has recently been made commercially available as Epogen, Amgen(California) and Procrit, Ortho Pharmaceuticals. Athletes have starting using erythropoietin in order to achieve the aforementioned effect. This is extremely dangerous as erythropoietin is a new, potent drug and it has already been linked to several recent deaths.

Clenbuterol is a b2-adrenoceptor agonist that has significant anabolic effects. Clenbuterol and other b2-adrenoceptor agonists have been used to enhance growth in farm animals.[81] However, this practice, due to consumer resistance, is not as widespread as some scientists think it should be. A significant number of consumers do not want to eat meat that has been chemically altered. Athletes, on the other hand, will eat almost anything that they believe will enhance their performance. Many athletes have added clenbuterol to their chemical arsenals. Athletes usually take 20 to 120 micrograms of clenbuterol per day. This is a small amount of drug, but it is detectable in the urine. The IOC put clenbuterol on the banned list on April 21, 1992. It is likely that athletes will be using a new, harder to detect b2-adrenoceptor agonist at the next Olympics. Jud Logan, a U.S. hammer thrower, and two British weight lifters, Andrew Davies and Andrew Saxton, were disqualified from the Barcelona Olympics after testing positive for clenbuterol. Saxton claimed that he was using the drug for asthma which is a common practice in Europe. The U.S. athlete has been banned for four years and the Brits may be banned for life. Either these athletes were not aware that clenbuterol had been put on the banned list or they were misinformed about clenbuterol's clearance time. Clenbuterol has a 35 hour half life in the human body. Thus, approximately 97% of the drug is removed from the body after 7 days. So an athlete that leaves an 8-9 day clearance time should have no problem passing a drug test.

Several experiments that document clenbuterol's effects on body weight, fat, and muscle have been done on rats. In one study[82] rats were divided into two groups. The first group was fed a powdered diet containing clenbuterol at the concentration of 4 mg/kg. The second group, the control group, was fed a normal powdered diet. The rats were allowed to eat as much as they desired over a period of 4 days then they were killed and autopsies were performed in order to document the results. On average, the rats that had been fed clenbuterol experienced a 29% increase in body weight. The rats hamstring, the largest rat muscle, mass increased by 14% and their heart mass increased by 12%. At the same time, epididymal fat pad weight decreased by 17%.

Clenbuterol has been promoted as a safe, effective alternative to anabolic steroids by many people. There is no doubt that clenbuterol is a highly effective muscle building agent. However clenbuterol, like most powerful drugs, can produces some negative side effects. The most serious of these side effects, as the rats demonstrate, is an increase in heart mass. The increase in cardiac muscle protein is associated with an increase in heart rate and is inhibited by a selective b1-antagonist, atenolol.[83]

Salbutamol is another b2-adrenoceptor agonist that has significant anabolic effects. Oral administration of slow release salbutamol causes significant increases in voluntary muscle strength in normal human volunteers within 2-3 weeks. All b2-adrenoceptor agonists do not exhibit significant anabolic effects. Salbutamol had to be modified into a slow release form in order to make it effective. It is likely that other b2-adrenoceptor agonists will also be modified in the near future in order to feed the never ending demand for performance enhancing drugs. At present, clenbuterol and cimaterol are the most powerful muscle building b2-adrenoceptor agonists available.

Oratic acid is a naturally occurring vitamin that can not be detected through current drug testing procedures. Oratic acid has been shown to have anabolic effects.

Zeranol is a potent anabolic agent commonly used to fatten cattle. It has been put on the banned list. A positive drug test for Zeranol could result from eating beef that contains Zeranol. As a result, it may be difficult to enforce the ban on this drug.

Ephedrine stimulates the heart and circulation, relieves hay fever, asthma, and nasal congestion, and decreases one's sensitivity to pain. Ephedrine comes from the Ephedra plant, which grows mainly in desert regions and is nicknamed the horsetail plant.[84] As early as 4,000 years ago Chinese emperors brewed ma huang tea from the Ephedra plant's leaves and flowers in order to utilize the plant's medicinal qualities. In the late nineteenth century scientists developed a synthetic form of ephedrine that they named amphetamine. Ephedrine is often used by athletes to increase energy and to reduce body fat. Recent studies have shown that using ephedrine while dieting helps to preserve muscle while reducing body fat.[85] Caffeine and aspirin make ephedrine more effective.

A study reported in the *International Journal of Obesity* monitored individuals who were taking 20 mg of ephedrine and 200 mg of caffeine 3 times daily. The participants in the study lost fat while preserving lean body mass. Withdrawal symptoms were not observed when use of the drugs was stopped. Serious side effects were not observed. However, minor side effects like tremor, agitation, insomnia, and increased sweating and nervousness were common. Potentially serious side effects like heart palpitations and tachycardia were observed, but they were found to be temporary. Extremely high doses of the ephedrine/caffeine stack could cause heart attacks in a small percentage of the population. The aforementioned dosages were found to be safe for most people.

The FDA recently restricted public access to ephedrine and the IOC put the drug on their banned list. It is no longer legal to sell ephedrine by itself. It has to be stacked with something. The problem was that some drug dealers were using pure ephedrine to manufacture speed. The regulatory agencies made it illegal to sell pure ephedrine because they wanted to make it more difficult for drug dealers to obtain the raw material required to make speed. Ephedrine is also legally available in the herb Ephedra, also known as Ma Huang, which naturally contains significant levels of ephedrine

A large number of products claim to increase testosterone and growth hormone levels naturally. Supposedly anabolic plants such as unicorn root, palmetto berries, yucca, yam extract, sarsaparilla leaf, schizandra, and astragalus have been promoted as legal sources of natural anabolic steroids. Some of these plants, such as sarsaparilla, may contain several steroids, but none function in an anabolic manner.[1] One company claims that its brand of yohimbine bark contains significant quantities of methyltestosterone. This is absolutely false as testosterone has never been detected in plant material of any kind.

Other companies claim that elements such as Boron can increase testosterone levels up to 300%. Once again, this is totally ridiculous. There was a study (*FASB J*, 1: 394-7, 1987) that reported that boron supplements increased testosterone in humans. What the advertisements do not tell you is that the study was conducted on postmenopausal women. Boron supplementation was found to increase both female and male hormones in postmenopausal women. The main consequence of this was decreased urinary excretion of phosphorus which indicates that boron may have a role in preventing osteoporosis, but not as a replacement for steroids.

Gamma hydroxy butyrate, GHB has been used by bodybuilders because it has been promoted by some as a fat burning muscle builder. GHB is produced by the body as a normal metabolite and is not a nutritional requirement. Claims have been made that GHB builds muscle by encouraging growth hormone release and or decreasing cortisol levels. GHB's fat burning/muscle building properties have not been conclusively proven.

GHB has been illegal in the United States since 1990. Prior to 1990 it was sold in many gyms and health food stores. Today GHB is being used by people that are not interested in bodybuilding. People are using GHB to get high. The GHB high is described by some as pleasurable, euphoric, sedating, and opiate like or heroin like but milder than heroin.

GHB can cause comas, seizures, increased muscle activity, and respiratory depression. Individuals that have taken 1/2-3 teaspoons of GHB dissolved in water may also experience vomiting, drowsiness, vertigo, and loss of consciousness. These effects usually come on 15-60 minutes after ingestion and can last up to 24 hours. No deaths have been reported as being caused solely by the use of GHB. However, some users have needed emergency room care and ventilator support or other intensive care.

GHB has been used to treat narcolepsy, as an anesthetic, and to treat ethanol withdrawal. GHB has been marketed under a number of names, including gama hydroxybutyric acid, sodium oxybate, sodium oxybutyrate, gamma hydroxybutyrate sodium, gamma-OH, 4-hydroxy butyrate, gammahydrate, and somatomax PM. GHB is distributed in powder or tablet form and is commonly dissolved in water. Some drug users have taken to mixing GHB and amphetamines in water to induce a trance like state.

Bodybuilders use niacin to enhance their appearance. Niacin does not promote muscular development, but it does cause blood to rush to the skin which produces vascularity and a red tint. Excessive amounts of niacin can produce severe headache, nausea, and peripheral nerve pain and the amount required to produce overdose symptoms can be quite small in susceptible individuals.

Carnitine is thought to enhance free fatty acid utilization. Enhancing free fatty acid utilization would improve performance because it allows the athlete to utilize his energy supply more efficiently. Carnitine also promotes the oxidation of pyruvate and several amino acids. This could theoretically decrease the production of lactic acid.

Lactic acid breaks down muscle and is a major cause of muscle aches and spasms that commonly occur after a strenuous workout. Lactic acid builds up to a higher degree in endurance athletes than in bodybuilders. However, controlling lactic acid build up is extremely beneficial for both groups of athletes because it allows them to keep more muscle.

Carnitine is synthesized in the liver and kidneys from the amino acids lysine and methionine. In addition, red meat and some dairy products contain significant amounts of carnitine. After ingestion and synthesis L-carnitine, the active form, is routed in the blood to heart and skeletal muscle which contains 98% of the body's L-carnitine.

Carnitine is part of the enzyme palmityltransferase which enables long-chain fatty acids to move through the cell membrane and into the cell. Energy is produced when individual cells process long-chain fatty acids. Hence, because it is known for a fact that carnitine plays a major role in enabling long-chain fatty acids to get into cells and be processed, it is not unreasonable to assume that carnitine could serve to increase an athlete's energy. Increased energy alone will not build muscle. In fact, it can cause one to over train which leads to muscle loss. However, a bodybuilder that is on a proper diet and has low energy would most likely experience muscle growth if his energy were increased as this would lead to longer, more intense workouts.

On the other hand it is possible that increasing the rate at which long-chain fatty acids get into cells for processing may not produce more energy. Studies have shown that muscle cells naturally contain enough carnitine to enable the palmityltransferase enzyme to function at its maximal rate. If this is true it would seem that exogenous carnitine intake would not lead to more energy. However, studies have also shown that exercise increases urinary excretion of carnitine and that during intense training it is possible that muscle carnitine levels may decrease. Unfortunately, there is disagreement over whether or not carnitine levels decrease to a point where supplementation would be beneficial.

If you decide to try carnitine you should make sure that the product you use contains the L-carnitine form. Another form of carnitine, D-carnitine is often found mixed with L-carnitine in commercial preparations. D-carnitine can cause muscle weakness and other harmful effects.

D-carnitine depletes L-carnitine stores in the tissues, thus creating symptoms of carnitine deficiency. An athlete that uses a supplement that contains both L and D carnitine may feel symptoms of carnitine deficiency when the use of the supplement is discontinued. The natural L-carnitine levels will have been depleted by the D-carnitine and there will no longer be any supplemental L-carnitine being administered. Some supplement companies do not want to spend the extra money required to produce nearly pure L-carnitine. Athletes using carnitine supplements should choose only products which are labeled as being 99% pure L-carnitine.

At this time there is not enough scientific data to support or reject the effectiveness of carnitine as an ergogenic aid. Of course, this is an ideal situation for supplement companies. Enough data exists to make it look like carnitine is an effective ergogenic even though it has not been proven that carnitine is an effective ergogenic.

Unknown a few years ago, oryzanol/ferulic acid (often called FRAC) is now widely used by strength/power athletes who believe it increases testosterone levels and promotes lean tissue by hypothalamic stimulation.

Oryzanol and ferulate are mixtures of ferulic acid esters of sterols extracted from rice bran, corn, and barley oils. Since plant sterols are metabolized in the gut tract and do not enter the blood intact, it is doubtful that these compounds have any muscle building or masculinizing effects.

A recent study found that body weight and shoulder press strength increased "significantly" in weightlifters receiving ferulate compared with those receiving a placebo (J Appl Sports Sci Res, 4:110, 1990). However, no differences were found in any other strength measures and the researches failed to monitor other activities of the subjects that could have caused the weight gain and shoulder press strength increase. In addition, the findings were reported in abstract form only and the findings have not been duplicated by other researchers.

Amino acid supplements are popular among weight lifters, body-builders, and endurance athletes. Proponents claim that certain amino acids increase muscle mass and decrease body fat. Endurance athletes say they need to replace specific amino acids that are metabolized during exercise.

Arginine and lysine are particularly popular as amino acid supplements because some studies have shown that they increase the secretion of growth hormone, thereby increasing muscle mass and decreasing body fat. However, in order to produce significant increases in growth hormone secretion these amino acids have to be taken in an extremely unpractical manner. Large doses, 20-30g intravenously, of arginine or lysine are required.

Arginine and lysine can be sold legally. However, it would be expensive and impractical to market these amino acids in the form that had been shown to work best. In addition, few consumers would be willing to spend the money and needle tolerance required to inject large doses of amino acids into their bodies. There is no conclusive evidence that the small amounts of amino acids provided by supplement manufacturers have any significant influence on serum growth hormone levels or body composition.

The debate is further confused by the fact that exercise itself increases growth hormone levels. When supplement companies conduct studies on their amino acid supplements intake of the supplements is combined with exercise. Growth hormone levels are monitored and shown to increase. Supplement companies claim that the supplement caused the increase in growth hormone levels. Independent researches consistently conclude that the resulting growth hormone increase was due solely to exercise.

Research on amino acid utilization during endurance exercise indicates that the branched chain amino acids (leucine, isoleucine, and valine) are the primary ones metabolized. These amino acids are important nitrogen sources for alanine, which may be converted to glucose for fuel via the alanine-glucose cycle.

Branched chain amino acids are essential amino acids which are found in complete animal proteins (meat, fish, fowl, dairy foods, and eggs) or by combining incomplete vegetable proteins (such as beans and rice or wheat). Since it is easy to obtain adequate branched chain amino acids in the diet, supplementation is not necessary.

Athletes on an energy-restricted diet who are not consuming adequate amounts of protein may benefit from a leucine supplement of 1 g/day; however, this should not be necessary with proper dietary counseling. Athletes who are spending a lot of money on lysine and arginine supplements should note that a 3-oz portion of lean roast beef has about 1,700 mg of arginine and 2,200 mg of lysine. It would take about 17 to 20 amino acid capsules or tablets to get comparable amounts!

Amino acid proponents claim that only a small percentage of the amino acids in food is digested and absorbed. Actually, about 95-99% of the amino acids from animal proteins, and about 90% of that from vegetable proteins, are absorbed and used by the body.

Proponents also assert that since amino acids do not need to be digested before absorption, they replenish the body's protein pool much faster. There is no evidence that faster absorption of amino acids is more beneficial. It takes hours, not minutes, to rebuild muscle protein that has been damaged during intense exercise.

Another claim is that supplements provide all of the amino acids provided by food, but in a form that is less taxing to the digestive system. The body readily produces an array of digestive enzymes that systematically break down food protein into amino acids before absorption. Thus, chicken or beans may be viewed as "time released" sources of amino acids.

The amount of amino acids in supplements is minimal. Usually about 200-500 mg per capsule. An ounce of beef, chicken, or fish provides 7 grams of protein-7,000 mg of amino acids!

Substituting amino acid supplements for food may cause deficiencies in other nutrients found in protein-rich foods, such as iron, niacin, and thiamin. In addition, large doses of amino acid supplements may cause amino acid imbalances and toxicity.

Many athletes don't realize that the body does not distinguish between amino acids obtained from food and those found in costly supplements. Excess amino acids which cannot be incorporated into new protein, muscle, are either burned for energy or converted to fat.

Amino acids are a class of organic compounds, some of which are the chief structures of proteins. Protein is essential for all people, not just athletes. Athletes can meet their protein requirements through a proper diet rather than spending money on expensive amino acid supplements.

Table 1. Dietary Supplement Requirements

Segment of Population (19 to 30 year olds)	Requirement (g protein per kg per day)
General population, 1989 US RDA	0.80
General population, 1990 Can. RNI	0.86
Resistance exercisers (male):	
Elite bodybuilders (steady state) 1.20	
Elite bodybuilders (increasing intensity)	1.40-1.70*
Elite weight lifters	1.60-1.76
Endurance exercisers:	
Elite, male	1.6
Well trained, male	1.2-1.4
Female	25%-35% lower than for male exercisers*

*Estimated.
RDA = recommended dietary allowance.
RNI = recommended nutrient intake.

Studies have demonstrated that the US RDA and Canadian RNI for protein are inadequate for many athletes. Estimated requirements for resistance athletes 1.2 to 1.6 g protein per kg per day are less than resistance athletes' reported habitual intakes of 2.5 to 3.0 g per kg per day. On the other hand, athletes who consume inadequate energy (such as dieters), protein (such as vegans), or carbohydrate may need to be aware of the increased need from exercise itself. The same is true for athletes for whom protein requirements are already increased, such as pregnant or lactating women.

Most athletes will meet the protein intakes recommended in table 1 provided that protein accounts for 10% of their diet and that food intake is adequate. For this reason, most endurance and resistance athletes do not need protein supplements.

Table 2. Protein Content of Some Common Foods

Food or Beverage	Energy (kcal)	Protein (g)
Whole wheat bread, 2 Slices	155	5.4
Spaghetti, 1.5 c plus 0.5 c Meatless spaghetti sauce	375	9.8
Potato, 2 medium, baked	290	6.1
Milk, 2% butterfat, 1 c	121	8.1
Beans, red kidney, 0.5 c	115	7.5
Sirloin steak, lean, 4 oz	250	32.5
Egg, whole, 2 large	158	12.1
Egg white, 2 large	32	6.7
Raisin bran cereal, 1.5 c	231	8.0

The most effective methods of increasing naturally occurring testosterone and growth hormone levels can not be packaged, patented, bought, or sold. Elevation of growth hormone levels during sleep is well documented. Sleep induced growth hormone elevation usually occurs during deep sleep. Deep sleep is characterized by dreaming and REM, rapid eye movement. A solid 8 hours of sleep provides the deep sleep required to promote sleep induced growth hormone elevation.

Moderate exercise increases testosterone and growth hormone levels. Testosterone and growth hormone levels tend to increase when strength training, e.g. weight lifting, sessions last from 30 to 60 minutes. If one is endurance training, e.g. running, testosterone and growth hormone levels tend to increase after exercise sessions lasting less than 2 hours and decrease if the exercise sessions last longer than 3 hours. Over training causes the body to process all of the testosterone and growth hormone being produced and stimulates the production of catabolic, tissue destroying, hormones. Training within the above mentioned time periods helps to promote growth by keeping testosterone and growth hormone levels high.

Sex, specifically sexual arousal is a strong stimulator of testosterone production. This is ironic as sexual activity among athletes has been discouraged in the past. A healthy sex life contributes greatly to the maintenance of optimum testosterone levels.

A proper diet is essential for maintaining optimum testosterone levels. Bodybuilders often need to lose weight to get ripped. However, low calorie diets depress testosterone levels. Bodybuilders should try to consume 1,500 to 2,000 calories a day while dieting. This is a low enough level of consumption to cause weight loss while it is high enough to keep testosterone levels from dropping. Eating too much fiber and not enough protein can also contribute to low testosterone levels. This is a common problem among vegetarian bodybuilders. People interested in maximizing testosterone should eat 0.8 to 1.5 grams of protein per kilogram of body weight (depending on activity level).

Winning has been shown to elevate testosterone levels. In one study college students either won or lost a $5 bet on a task controlled entirely by chance. The students that won the bet reported a more positive mood change than did the losers. After the bet testosterone levels were measured. The winners exhibited significantly higher testosterone levels than the losers.

Depression and stress have been shown to decrease testosterone levels and increase cortisol, a catabolic (tissue destroying), hormone. One study monitored testosterone and cortisol levels in severely depressed individuals. the study found that male patients secrete less testosterone during acute depression than after clinical remission. In addition, cortisol levels were found to decrease following recovery. Stress, an emotion often associated with depression, produces similar results. Exercise has been shown to decrease stress and depression. This is another reason why exercise helps to keep testosterone at optimum levels.

Sun light helps to stimulate testosterone production. Laying out in the sun is an extremely popular for of relaxation. The stress relieving properties of sun bathing may be responsible for the testosterone elevation observed in individuals that laid out for 20-30 minutes. There is also some speculation that sun light itself may stimulate a physiological reaction that leads to elevated testosterone levels. Laying out 2 to 3 times a week for 20-30 minutes provides sufficient stimulation. Excessive sunbathing should be avoided as this can lead to skin cancer.

Testosterone and growth hormone levels decrease with age. Continuing to exercise helps to keep the body young and will keep testosterone and growth hormone at optimum levels even among older individuals. Staying active in other areas may also help older individual maintain optimum testosterone and growth hormone levels. The striving achievement of early adulthood may contribute to higher testosterone and growth hormone levels among younger individuals. While it is likely that the quieter time of middle adulthood leads to decreases in testosterone and growth hormone among older individuals.

It has been known for at least 200 years that skeletal muscle contracts when stimulated by electricity. Electrical muscle stimulation can be used to maintain and or build muscle. However, it is not as efficient or effective as working out. A healthy bodybuilder can work his muscle sufficiently by working out a few hours a day. There is no need to slap on some electric pads and shock ones muscles into contractions while reading or watching television. In fact, many bodybuilders limit their gains by overworking their muscles. Something that is easy to do in the gym and even easier to do when hooked up to an electrical muscle stimulating machine that concentrates on small areas of muscle. This is why you do not see every other bodybuilder hooked up to one of these machines for several hours a day.

Knowing when to stop working out and let muscle rest and recuperate is an essential part of bodybuilding. Working out too much will destroy muscle. The idea that one could just sit around hooked up to an electrical muscle simulating machine for eight hours a day and get huge is ridiculous. When muscles are over worked all of the anabolic, tissue building, hormones in the body get used up. Then, the catabolic, tissue destroying hormones start to dominate. Anabolic and catabolic hormones bind to the same receptors in the muscle. When the muscle is overworked the receptor sites fill up with catabolic hormones and the muscle starts to deteriorate.

Anabolic hormones get used up after every workout. Rest is required to give the body time to build the level of anabolic hormones back up. When people use anabolic steroids they artificially bypass this natural limitation of the body. They are able to workout longer, harder, heavier, and require less rest. The end result of their artificial advantage is freaky big cartoon like muscle that can not be maintained by over the counter supplements or electrical muscle stimulation. It can only be obtained and maintained by continuing to boost up the level of anabolic hormones in the body while keeping the level of catabolic hormones as low as possible.

Even a juiced up bodybuilder needs a sufficient amount of rest between workouts. After sufficient rest muscle can be worked again and new muscle growth may take place. Hence, use of an electrical muscle stimulating machine by someone that is already working out would most likely lead to muscle deterioration, not muscle growth.

Anyone who bought an electrical muscle stimulating machine under the illusion that it would be the key to making them huge would be sorely disappointed. However, electrical muscle stimulation is being used by some athletes to maintain and or build muscle. When an athlete is injured in such a way that he can no longer workout, a joint may be injured and require a cast that prevents bending of the joint, electrical stimulation is often used to preserve or restore the pre-injury state of the skeletal muscle.

When working out one has to bend the knee in order to work the hamstring. With electrical muscle stimulation a pad can be placed on the hamstring and it can be worked without involving the knee. Three sessions a weak of high frequency electrical stimulation have been shown to maintain skeletal muscle. For an injured athlete this translates to reduced muscle deterioration and decreased recovery time following injury and or surgery. Once one has recovered to the point where working out does not re-damage the injury electrical muscle stimulation is discontinued. Working out, when it can be done without causing further damage, is always the preferred method of muscle rehabilitation. It is safer and more effective than electrical muscle stimulation. Electrical muscle stimulation, if done incorrectly, (too much electricity used for too long) can result in injury. In addition, it is not yet known whether proper regular use of electrical muscle stimulation over a period of years causes damage.

One of the most powerful tools for increasing the production of endogenous testosterone is the brain. The power of the mind should not be underestimated. The placebo effect, benefiting from a drug that has no medical value, exemplifies the tremendous potential that is locked inside each and every human brain. Doctors have documented the improvement of medical conditions in patients that thought they were receiving effective medication, when they were actually receiving a placebo, a substance that has no medical value. The patients benefited because they believed that they were receiving treatments that would cure them. This belief caused their brains to take actions to fix their conditions. Positive thought can be used to build muscle just as it can be use to cure illness. Miraculous recoveries of patients that were diagnosed with deadly, incurable cancers have been attributed to a positive state of mind. Exactly how the brain is able to cure these things that doctors think are incurable is not known. What is known is that people who go through such experiences say that they knew all along that they were going to win their battles. They had focused minds and they succeeded.

CONCLUSION

Anabolic steroids are potent drugs that have a wide range of positive and negative effects. As with other illegal drugs, attempts at curtailing anabolic steroid use have not been successful. Large numbers of people are using anabolic steroids. The law, by preventing studies of anabolic steroid use at dosages that athletes use, has made anabolic steroid use more dangerous than it should be.

While anabolic steroids are used by a wide range of athletes, bodybuilding is, by far, the sport that is most connected with anabolic steroids. Professional bodybuilding attracts attention because professional bodybuilders are freaky big. One becomes some what immune to the amazing size that pro bodybuilders achieve after reading muscle magazines for a few years. However, many people can still remember the amazement they experienced the first time they saw a truly huge bodybuilder flexing cartoon like muscle. Such a sight is impressive and it commands attention. It also causes most people to think, at least in the back of their minds, that such muscles could not have been obtained naturally. A few years ago I was at the newsstand looking through the muscle magazines. A young boy, he must have been around 5 or 6, happened to walk up and pick up one of the muscle mags. He flipped to the middle of the magazine. In what may have been the first time that he ever saw a professional bodybuilder he said aloud, to himself, "No way! These guys must be on hemorrhoids." He didn't have a full vocabulary yet, but he knew the truth about professional bodybuilding.

If professional bodybuilders did not use anabolic steroids they would not look much different from other healthy, fit individuals. Assuming that one eats right, doesn't overtrain, and gets enough sleep, there is only one factor that limits growth. The ratio of tissue building to tissue destroying hormones present. Anabolic steroids artificially raise the level of tissue building hormones in the body. This allows one to grow beyond

107

the point that one's body would naturally permit. Supplements do not do this and they never will. Any substance that produced such a powerful effect would, after becoming popular, be regulated by the Food and Drug Administration and or the Drug Enforcement Agency.

The best, most effective supplements out there are merely fancy forms of reconstituted food. They produce minute benefits that can easily be obtained through a proper diet. Most of the supplements on the market, even though they are frequently endorsed by steroid monsters when advertised, are completely worthless. When people see such ads they often wonder if the supplement helped make the pictured steroid monster huge. They should be wondering how much the steroid monster got paid to endorse the product.

Many years have passed since *Pumping Iron* brought the steroid built bodies of Arnold and Franco to the attention of the public. As the years went by, countless new, amazing, steroid replacing products were introduced, but steroids remain in a category all their own.

END NOTES

[1]Murad, F and Haynes, RC Jr: "The Pharmacologic Basis of Therapeutics," 7th ed. Macmillan, New York, 1986, p 1440.

[2]De Kruif, P: "The Male Hormone," Harcourt, Brace and Company, 1945.

[3]"Hitler's final days recalled by physician," Am. Med News, October, 1985.

[4]Michael, G and Baulieu, EE: "Androgen receptor in rat skeletal muscle: characterization and phsioligical variations," Endocrinology, 107:2088-94,1980.

[5]Gooren, L and Kaas, P: "Safety aspects of androgen therapy," Springer-Verlag, Berlin Heidelberg, 182-203, 1990.

[6]Gooren, L and Kaas, P: "Safety aspects of androgen therapy," Springer-Verlag, Berlin Heidelberg, 182-203, 1990.

[7]Petry, R, Rausch-Strohmann, J, Hienz, H, Senge, T, and Mauss, J: "Androgen treatment without inhibition effect on hypophysis and male gonads, Acta Endocrinology, 59: 497-507, 1968.

[8]Alkalay, D, Khemani, L, Wagner, W, Bartlett, M: "Sublingual and oral administration of methyltestosterone. A comparison of drug bioavailability," J Clin Pharmac, 13: 142-151, 1973.

[9]Nieschlag, E, Behre, H, and Weinbauer, G: "Hormonal methods for the regulation of male fertility," Serono Symposia, Vol. 53, Raven Press, New York, p. 517-529, 1989.

[10]Francis, C: "Speed Trap," St. Martin's Press, New York, 1990.

[11]Nieschlag, E, Behre, H, and Weinbauer, G: "Hormonal methods for the regulation of male fertility," Serono Symposia, Vol. 53, Raven Press, New York, p. 517-529, 1989.

[12]Frey, H, Askvag, A, Saanum, D, and Falch, J: "Bioavailablilty of oral testosterone in males," Eur J Clin Pharmacol, 16: 345-349, 1979.

[13]Nieshlag, E, Mauss, J, Coert, A, and Kicovic, P: "Plasma androgen levels in men after oral administration of testosterone or testosterone undecanoate, Acta endocrinol, 79: 336, 1975.

[14]Nieschlag, E, Behre, H, and Weinbauer, G: "Hormonal methods for the regulation of male fertility," Serono Symposia, Vol. 53, Raven Press, New York, p. 517-529, 1989.

[15]Rajalakshmi, M and Ramakrinshanan, P: "Pharmacokinetics and pharmacodynamics of a new long-acting androgen ester: maintenance of physiological androgen levels for 4 months after a single injection," Contraception 40: 399-412, 1989.

[16]Handelsman, D, Conway A, and Boylan, L: "Pharmacokinetics and pharmacodynamics of testosterone pellets in man," J Clin Endocrinol Mtab 71: 216-222, 1990.

[17]Nieschlag, E, Behre, H, and Weinbauer, G: "Hormonal methods for the regulation of male fertility," Serono Symposia, Vol. 53, Raven Press, New York, p. 517-529, 1989.

[18]Bhasin, S: "Microencapsulated testosterone. Presentation at the Workshop Conference on Androgen Therapy," Marco Island, Florida, 1990.

[19]Feldmann, R and Maibach, H: " Regional variation in percutaneous penetration of 14 C cortisol in man," J Invest Dermatol, 48: 181-183, 1967.

[20]Bals-Pratsch, M, Langer, K, Place, V, and Nieschlag, E: "Substitution therapy of hypogonadal men with transdermal testosterone over one year," Acta Endocrinal 118: 7-13, 1988.

[21]Delanoe, D, Fougeyrollas, B, Meyer, L, and Thonneau, P: "Androgenisation of female partners of men on medroxy-progesterone acetate/percutaneous testosterone contraception," Lancet i: 276, 1984.

[22]Nieschlag, E, Cuppers, H, Wiegelmann, W, and Wickings, E: "Bioavailability and LH-suppressing effect of different testosterone preparations in normal and hypogonadal men," Hormone Research, 7: 13, 1976.

[23]Danner, C, and Fric, G: "Androgen substitution with testosterone-containing nasal drops," Int J Androl, 3: 429-431, 1980.

[24]Hickson, RC: "Skeletal Muscle Cytosol (3h)Methyl Trienolone Receptor Binding and Serum Androgens, Effects of Hypertrophy and Hormonal State," J Steroid Biochem 19:1705, 1983.

[25]Hickson, RC and Kurowski, TG: "Anabolic Steroids and Training," Clin Sports Med 5:461, 1986.

[26]Wadler, GI and Hainline, B: "Drugs and the Athlete," F. A. Davis Company, Philadelphia, 1989.

[27]Hatfield, F: "Anabolic steroids: What kind and how many," Fitness System, Venice, California, 1982.

[28]Hatfield, F: "Anabolic steroids: What kind and how many," Fitness System, Venice, California, 1982.

[29]Wright, J: "Anabolic steroids and sport II," Natick, Massachusetts, Sports Science Consultants, 1982.

[30]Wadler, GI and Hainline, B: "Drugs and the Athlete," F. A. Davis Company, Philadelphia, 1989.

[31]Goldman, B: "Death in the Locker Room," The Body Press, Tucson, 1987.

[32]Taylor, W: "Macho Medicine," McFarland, North Carolina, 1991.

[33]Sholl, S, Goy, R, and Kim, K: "5a-reductase, aromatase, and androgen receptor levels in the monkey brain during fetal development," Endocrinology, 124: 627-34, 1989.

[34]Pope, H and Katz, D: "Bodybuilders psychosis," Lancet, 1987, April.

[35]Pope, H and Katz, D: "Effective and psychotic symptoms associated with anabolic steroid use," *American J Psychiatry*, 1988, 145(4), p. 487-490.

[36]Wright, J:"The Feds Crack Down," Muscle and Fitness, August 1992, p. 94.

[37]Nieschlag, E, Behre, H, and Weinbauer, G: "Hormonal methods for the regulation of male fertility," Serono Symposia, Vol. 53, Raven Press, New York, p. 517-529, 1989.

[38]Johnson, FS: "The Association of Oral Androgenic-Anabolic Steroids and Life-Threatening disease," Med Sci Sports, 7:284, 1975.

[39]Wright, J and Cowart, V: "Anabolic Steroids, Altered States," Carmel, Indiana, Benchmark Press, 1990.

[40]Bagheri, S and Boyer, J: "Peliosis hepatis associated with androgenic anabolic steroid therapy. A sever form of hepatic injury," Ann Int Med, 81: 6106-18, 1974.

[41]Schiff, L: "Diseases of the Liver," fourth ed., J. B. Lippincott Company, 1977.

[42]Eberle, A, Sparrow, J, and Keenan, B: "Treatment of persistent pubertal gynecomastia with dihydrotestosterone heptanoate,"Pediatr, 109(1): 144-9,1986.

[43]Parker, L, Gray, D, Lai, M, and Levin, E: "Treatment of gynecomastia with tamoxifen: a double blind crossover study," Metabolism, 35: 705-8, 1986.

[44]Mauss, J and Borsch, K: "Effect of Long Term Testosterone Oenanthate Administration on Male Reproductive Function," Acta Endocrine., 1975.

[45]Waites, G: "Diczfalusy E, Griffin P, Khanna J Research in Human Reproduction, Biennial Report 1986-1987, World Health Organization, Geneva, p 199-227, 1988.

[46]Prat, J, Gray, G, Stolley, P, and Coleman, J: "Wilms tumor in an adult associated with androgen abuse," JAMA, 237: 2322-3, 1977

[47]Gooren, L and Kaas, P: "Safety aspects of androgen therapy," Springer-Verlag, Berlin Heidelberg, 182-203, 1990.

[48]Meer, J: "Drugs and Sports," Chelsea House, New York, 1987.

[49]Thompson, P, Culinane, E, Sady, S, Chenevert, C, Saritelli, A, Sady, M, and Herbert, P: "Contrasting effects of testosterone and stanozolol on serum lipoprotein levels," J of the Amer Med Ass, 261: 1165-1168, 1989.

[50]Roberts, J and Essnhigh, D: "Adenocarcinoma of Prostate in 40-Year Old Bodybuilder," Lancet, 2:742, 1984.

[51]Freed, D, Banks, J, Longson, D, and Burley, D: "Anabolic Steroids in Athletics: Crossover Double-Blind Trial on Weight Lifters," Brit. Med. J., 1975.

[52]Hamilton, J: "The role of testicular secretions as indicated by the effects of castration in man and by studies of pahthological conditions and the short life span associated with maleness," Recent Progress in Hormone Research, 3, 257-322, 1948.

[53]Goldman, B: "Death in the Locker Room," The Body Press, Tucson, Arizona, 1984.

[54]Taylor, W: "Hormonal Manipulation," McFarland & Co., Jefferson, N.C., 1985.

[55]Taken from the insert that Ciba Pharmaceutical enclosed with Dianabol.

[56]Taken from the insert that Ciba Pharmaceutical enclosed with Dianabol.

[57]Gooren, L and Kaas, P: "Safety aspects of androgen therapy," Springer-Verlag, Berlin Heidelberg, 182-203, 1990.

[58]Wright, J and Cowart, V: "Anabolic Steroids, Altered States," Carmel, Indiana, Benchmark Press, 1990.

[59]Di Pasquale, M: "Drug Use & Detection in Amateur Sports," M.G.D. Press, Ontario, 1984.

[60]Eichelberger, C: "Drug Vigilance is Intensifying," The Sacramento Bee, Tuesday, July 14, 1992.

[61]Taylor, W: "Macho Medicine," McFarland, North Carolina, 1991.

[62] Taken form the "Steroid Trafficking Act of 1990".

[63]Kammerer, R: "Anabolic Steroid Testing," Brute Enterprises, August, 1992.

[64]Taylor, W: "Macho Medicine," McFarland, North Carolina, 1991.

[65]Morttram, D: "Drugs in Sport," Human Kinetics Books, Illinois, 1988.

[66]Taylor, W: "Macho Medicine," McFarland, North Carolina, 1991.

[67]Biggane, B: "Numerous ways around testing," Cox News Services, August 22, 1991.

[68]Colgan, M: "Human Growth Hormone," Advanced Research Press, July, 1992.

[69]Brown, P: "Potential epidemic of Creutzfeld-Jacob disease from human growth hormone therapy," New England Journal of Medicine, 1985.

[70]"Science News," 1990.

[71]"Physicians Desk Reference 41 Edition," Medical Economics, Oradell, New Jersey, 1987,970.

[72]Physicians Desk Reference 41 Edition," Medical Economics, Oradell, New Jersey, 1987,970.

[73]Rosenfeld, R: "Methionyl human growth hormone and oxandrolone in Tuners syndrome," J Pediatr, 1986.

[74]Gerner, J: "Renewed catch-up growth with increased replacement doses of human growth hormone," J Pediatr, 1987.

[75]Crist, D: "Body composition response to exogenous GH during training in highly conditioned adults," J Appl Physiol, 1988.

[76]Todd, T: "The use of human growth hormone poses a grave dilemma," Sports Illustrated, 1984.

[77]Colgan, M: "Human Growth Hormone," Advanced Research Press, July, 1992.

[78]Linfoot, J: "Acromegaly and giantism," In Daughaday W.H.(Ed), Endocrine Control of Growth, New York, Elsevier, 1981.

[79]Goldman, B: "Death in the Locker Room," The Body Press, Tucson, 1987.

[80]Goldman, B: "Death in the Locker Room," The Body Press, Tucson, 1987.

[81]Williams,P: "The use of b-agonists as a means of altering body composition in livestock species," Nutr Abstr Rev, 57: 453-64, 1987.

[82]Choo, J, Horan, M, Little, R, and Rothwell, N: "Anabolic effects of clenbuterol on skeletal muscle are mediated by b2-adrenoceptor activation," Amer J Phys, E50-E55, July 1992.

[83]Hebert, F, Hovell, F, and Reeds, P: "Some preliminary observations on the immediate effects of clenbuterol on heart rate...," Proc Nutr Soc, 45: 105A, 1985.

[84]Dolan, E: "Drugs in Sport," Franklin Watts, New York, p. 44, 1986.

[85]Dulloo, A and Miller, D: "Ephedrine, caffeine, and aspirin: over-the-counter drugs that interact to stimulate thermogenesis in the obese," Nutrition, 5: 7, 1989.

INDEX

Symbols

17 a position 34
20Aet-1 15, 16
4-hydroxy butyrate 94
5a-reductase 110

A

A.P.L. 62
Abdomen 38
Abdominal wall 19
Abuse potential 45
Acne 23, 38, 40, 60, 61
Acromegaly 88
Adam's Apple 39
Adolescent female 40
Adolescents 87
Adrenal Gland Concentrate 69
Aerobic endurance 37, 89
Aerobics 63, 79
Aggression 31, 61
Agitation 92
AIDS 41
Alanine-glucose cycle 97
Alcohol 18, 31, 51, 67
Alcoholism 18
Alkalay, D 109
Alkyl group 34
Alternatives to anabolic steroids 86
Amgen 89
Amino acids 97
Amphetamines 43, 45, 94
Amygdaloid nucleus 31
Anabolic 9
Anabolic steroid metabolites 54
Anabolic Steroid News. 59

Anadrol 71
Anadrol-50 14, 28, 75
Anaphylactic shock 39
Anavar 10, 13, 41, 54, 55, 63
Androgen receptors 31
Androgen therapy 111
Androgenic 9, 38
Androgenisation 110
Andropause 17
Androstenedione 12
Androviron 12
Anemia 28
Anesthetic 93
Animal proteins 97
Animals 48
Anti-catabolic 27
Anti-estrogens 43
Antibody formation 88
Antidepressants 31
Ape-man 88
Appetite 23
Arginine 96
Aristocort 43
Arms 60
Arnold 68, 108
Aromatase 110
Aromatize 36
Arrhythmia 77
Arthritis 43
Askvag, A 109
Aspirin 92
Assellacrin 86
Asthma 90, 91
Astragalus 92
Atenolol 91
Athletes 53, 87

Australia 19

B

B1-antagonist 91
B2-adrenoceptor 91
B2-agonists 67
Back 38
Bacteria 86
Bagheri, S 111
Baldness 38, 40
Bals-Pratsch, M 110
Banks, J 111
Barbiturates 45
Barcelona Olympics 90
Barley 96
Bartlett, M 109
Basal metabolic 63
Basketball 87
Baulieu, E 109
Beans 97, 98
Bed nucleus 31
Beef 98
Behavioral changes 31, 37
Behre, H 109
Belle International 59
Benaziza 43
Benchmark Press 110
Berlin 109
Betamethasone 43
Bhasin, S 109
Biggane, B 112
Bile 34, 35
Bioavailability 110
Biodegradable microspheres 20
Bitch tits 62
Black-market 13, 39, 46, 47, 52, 86, 87
Blackballed 65
Bladder 53
Blood 11
Blood cells 37
Blood pressure 30, 37

Blood stream 10, 11
Blood tests 64
Blood vessels 18
Body analysis machine 63
Body bag 78
Body fat 87
Body fat test 63
Body image 30
Body weight 59
Bodybuilder 38, 43
Bodybuilders 42, 51, 53, 87, 94
Bodybuilding 32, 50, 85
Bodybuilding magazines 50
Boils 67
Boldenone 54
Bone closure 41
Bone growth 40, 68
Bone marrow 37
Bones 70
Boron 69, 93
Borsch, K 111
Boxing 78
Boyer, J 111
Boylan, L 109
Brace and Company 109
Brain 21, 25, 31, 86, 104
Branched chain amino acids 97
Breast 40
Breast development 35
British 90
Brower 33
Brown, P 112
Bruising 35
Bumex 77
Burley, D 111

C

Caffeine 63, 92
Calf raises 60
California 89
Calories 61, 87

114

116

123

Smuggling 47
Sodium 77
Sodium oxybutyrate 94
Solidness 69
Somatomax PM 94
Somatomedin-C 55
Southern California 55
Spaghetti 100
Spain 46
Sparrow, J 111
Speed 92
Speed bags 78
Sperm 35, 36
Sperm levels 36
Spiropent 72
Sports 87
Sports Illustrated 112
Springer-Verlag 109
Squat 59
Stacking 24, 32
Stair master 78
Stanolone 54
Stanozolol 11, 14, 28, 54, 55, 60, 61, 63
Sternum 40
Steroid counterfeits 47
Steroid dealer 45
Steroid experiences 59
Steroid monsters 108
Steroid receptor sites 21
Steroid replacing products 108
Steroid Trafficking Act of 1990 45
Sterols 96
Stolley, P 111
Strength 7, 21, 60, 62
Strength training 101
Stress 102
Stria terminalis 31
Stroke 42
Sun light 102
Sunbathing 102
Supplement 27, 69
Supplement ads 50

Supplement companies 96
Supplement manufacturers 97
Supplementation 97
Supplements 50, 75, 85
Suppositories 21
Surgery 104
Sweating 92
Sydney 19
Synthetic anabolic steroids 11
Synthetic HGH 87
Syringe 39, 42

T

Tablets 60
Tachycardia 92
Tall 87
Tamoxifen 35, 43
Tax payers 47
Taylor, W 110
Tea 91
Teenagers 7, 41, 68
Tendon 39
Tendon rupture 39
Tendons 88
Teslac 28, 36
Testes 21, 35, 36, 54
Testex 15, 28
Testicular atrophy 35, 36, 39, 43, 89
Testicular secretions 111
Testicular size 23
Testing facility 76
Testoject-50 28
Testolactone 28, 54
Testosterone
    9, 10, 12, 21, 28, 29, 35, 36, 40, 54, 89
Testosterone creams 20
Testosterone cyclohexanecarboxylate
    14, 15
Testosterone cypionate 14, 15, 28, 32, 67
Testosterone enanthate 14, 15, 28, 36
Testosterone ester 13, 14

Weinbauer, G 109
Well-being 18
Wheat 97
White heads 38
Whole wheat bread 100
Wickings, E 110
Williams, Horace 32
Williams,P 112
Wilm's tumor 37
Winning 102
Winstrol 11, 14, 28, 55
Withdrawal 30, 72
Withdrawal depression 31
Women 9
Workout 69
World Health Organization 15, 36, 42
World War II 9
Wright, J 110
Wrist nerve pain 88

X

Xiphoid 40

Y

Yam extract 92
Yohimbine bark 92
Yucca 92
Yugoslavia 46

Z

Zeranol 91
Ziegler, Dr. John 29
Zits 38